SOME ASPECTS
OF AMERICA'S
TEXTILE INDUSTRY

With Special Reference To Cotton

By

WILLIAM HAYS SIMPSON

Department of Political Science

Duke University

DIVISION OF GENERAL STUDIES
UNIVERSITY OF SOUTH CAROLINA
COLUMBIA

Manufactured In The
UNITED STATES OF AMERICA
By THE R. L. BRYAN COMPANY
COLUMBIA, SOUTH CAROLINA

To

JOHN NOEL SIMPSON, JR.

INTRODUCTION

Few scholars are as familiar with the history, development, and current problems of the cotton textile industry in the United States as is Dr. William Hays Simpson. Some years ago he published two studies dealing with the general subject, "Life in Mill Communities" and "Southern Textile Communities." For more than thirty-five years he has been a faculty member at one of the great universities in the heart of the textile-producing area. He has taken full advantage of this opportunity to observe closely the many changes that have taken place on this important part of the business scene. I know of no person not actually employed in the industry whom I regard as so knowledgeable about it.

All those concerned with the present and future of this significant section of the American economy will welcome this latest volume. In it Dr. Simpson has provided a documented picture of the textile field today, and has indicated his beliefs about necessary future steps to be taken if the industry is to survive.

All of us are grateful to him for his endeavors.

NICHOLAS P. MITCHELL, *Dean,*
College of General Studies,
University of South Carolina.

April, 1966

PREFACE

The making of cotton cloth began with the early settlements in America to care for the needs of the family. Later, however, about the end of the eighteenth century cotton cloth became an important item of trade. With the establishment of Slater's Mill cotton manufacturing entered a new era and during the decades which followed numerous cotton mills were built in New England. Toward the middle of the nineteenth century the first mills were established in the South and by 1900 they had spread throughout the area. Today the industry, while dispersed over a large area, is concentrated in the cotton producing states.

Textile manufacturing constitutes at the present time one of the most important industries in the United States. Presently America ranks first in the number of active spindles, and enjoys the most modern equipment of all countries of the world. In fact the scope of the industry has become so great and its problems so multitudinous that it seemed feasible to limit the extent of this study.

During the decade 1940-1950, I completed two studies "Life in Mill Communities" and "Southern Textile Communities." A few years later, I visited cotton mill areas in England, Holland and Canada and wrote a series of articles, published in the *Textile Bulletin* during 1953 and 1954, on the social and economic life of textile workers in those areas. During the course of these studies I talked with many textile mill executives and operatives. These contacts, added to the fact that I have lived most of my life in a cotton mill area, aroused my interest in the industry and resulted in this work.

To obtain information relative to this study I have visited textile mills in Massachusetts, Rhode Island, North and South Carolina, Georgia and Alabama and have conferred with numerous persons interested in the industry. Officials of the various textile associations have been very cooperative in giving assistance when requested, and staff members of textile schools have been most helpful. I am also indebted to officials of the Departments of Commerce and of Agriculture for printed and mimeographed material which they so generously supplied me.

A visit to the American Textile Machinery Exhibition in Atlantic City, in 1965, afforded an opportunity to see in operation hundreds of the latest model textile machines and to note the development of that related industry.

Materials in the Library of the School of Textiles at North Carolina State University were most valuable and the Library staff was very helpful.

I wish to express my great appreciation for grants from the Ford Foundation Committee on Research in Public Affairs and the Duke University Council on Research which made possible the completion of this study.

I am greatly indebted to Mrs. C. W. Ralston for reading the manuscript and for making helpful suggestions and to Mrs. Kent E. Mast for assistance in typing.

The author alone is responsible, however, for all statements and expressions of opinion in this study.

WILLIAM HAYS SIMPSON

Duke University
March, 1966

TABLE OF CONTENTS

TABLES

ix

TABLES—*Continued*

CHAPTER I

HISTORICAL DEVELOPMENT

Beginning with the early settlements in America, ideas were advanced for the manufacture of cotton. This may be noted in the Journal of Governor Winthrop, June, 1643.

> Our supplies from England failing very much, men began to look about them and fell to the manufacture of cotton, whereof we had a store from Barbadoes, and of hemp and flax, wherein Rowley, to their commendation, exceeded all other towns.[1]

During the century which followed, the manufacture of cotton was not only a home industry to care for the needs of the family, but it also was an important item of trade. It was not, however, until the last decade of the eighteenth century that the manufacture of cotton reached an important position in the United States.

Progress in the manufacture of cotton was limited because of the lack of capital and labor and because of restrictive legislation passed by the Parliament of England designed to prohibit the export of new machinery for carding, drawing and spinning cotton invented by Hargreave, Compton and Arkwright.[2] Efforts on the part of the Government of Massachusetts in 1786 and 1787 and the Pennsylvania Society for the Encouragement of Arts and Domestic Manufacturers in 1788 to procure these inventions were unsuccessful.[3] During the period, however, numerous small cotton manufacturing concerns were established in New England and the Middle Atlantic states. The movement reached South Carolina and, in 1770, a committee with Henry Lawrens as chairman raised a considerable sum of money to establish and promote manufacturing in the province and to circulate petitions to raise money for the enterprise. Later, in 1795, the General Assembly of South Carolina passed an Act providing for a lottery to raise 400 pounds to aid William McClure in establishing a cotton manufactory.[4] Pennsylvania and other states lent similar assistance to cotton manufacturing enterprises.[5]

---

[1] W. R. Bagnall, *The Textile Industries of the United States,* Vol. I, p. 6.
[2] W. B. Wesdon, *Economic and Social History of New England, 1620-1789,* Vol. II, p. 848.
[3] W. R. Bagnall, *op. cit.,* Vol. II, pp. 75-76.
[4] August Kohn, *The Cotton Mills of South Carolina,* p. 6.
[5] W. R. Bagnall, *The Textile Industries of the United States,* Vol. I, p. 78.

A number of jinny mills, run by hand or horse power, were established. The first of these factories, started in Philadelphia in 1787, was, however, destroyed by fire in 1790.[6] A larger mill, also started in 1787, was built in Beverly, Massachusetts, and was operated by horse power. It was exempted from taxation, subsidized by the legislature, and given state land and $4,000 in benefits from a lottery; but the enterprise was a failure and ceased operation in 1807.[7]

Attempts to invent water frames to manufacture cotton in America failed. The Barr brothers, aided by a subsidy granted by the Massachusetts Legislature, developed a set of machines called "State Models" which were put on exhibition. Frames, however, copied from these models never worked.[8]

Fortunately for the American cotton industry, young Samuel Slater noted in an English newspaper inducements offered by the legislatures of Pennsylvania and other states to encourage the development of machines to manufacture cotton. He therefore made a careful study of cotton manufacturing machines and emigrated to America disguised as a farm worker. (The disguise was necessary for him to be allowed to emigrate due to the strict ban by Parliament on exportation of machinery.) After a short stay in New York, Slater, upon invitation of Moses Brown, went to Pawtucket, Rhode Island, where he constructed machinery like that then in use in England. His spindles, driven by water, were put into operation early in 1791, thus marking the real beginning of cotton manufacture in America.[9] While this mill had only 72 spindles, it was for several years the only successful machine spinner of cotton in this country. However, before the end of the century similar establishments operated at New Haven, Wrenthans, New York City, Warwick, Paterson, East Hartford, Suffield, Wilmington, Philadelphia and Reheboth.[10] The mills at New York, Paterson, Philadelphia and Wilmington operated but a short time, so that in 1800 the factory at Beverly and seven Arkwright mills (four near Providence and three in Connecticut) made up the organized cotton industry of America. It is estimated that they operated less than 2,000 spindles and annually spun between 50,000 and 100,000 pounds of imported cotton into yarn for general sale.[11]

---

[6] Ibid., p. 79.

[7] Ibid., pp. 89-100; C. F. Ware, The Early New England Cotton Manufacture, p. 20.

[8] W. R. Bagnall, The Textile Industries of the United States, Vol. I, pp. 85-86.

[9] C. F. Ware, The Early New England Cotton Manufacture, p. 21; V. S. Clark, History of Manufactures in the United States, Vol. I, p. 535.

[10] W. R. Bagnall, op. cit., Vol. I, pp. 172, 185, 189-90, 213-215, 241-242, 244, 250, 251.

[11] V. S. Clark, History of Manufactures in the United States, Vol. I, p. 535.

The industry grew in New England and by 1804 the number of mills had more than doubled in Rhode Island and Connecticut and new ones were established in Massachusetts, New Hampshire and New York.[12]

The Embargo of 1807, the Non-Intercourse Act, and the War of 1812 practically eliminated English cotton goods from the American scene. Local industry, therefore, developed to meet the demands of population, and high prices of cotton cloth attracted investors.[13]

While the establishment of cotton mills was in full stride in New England, some small steps were taken in the South to develop the cotton industry. The South Carolina legislature passed an appropriation bill in 1809 which provided for the advancement of $1,000 to Ephraim McBryde to enable him to construct a spinning machine on the principles mentioned in a patent he held from the United States. In the same year, however, the request of the president of the Homespun Company of South Carolina for a loan on account of a patent was unfavorably reported by a legislative committee; but the committee recommended that he be allowed until the next meeting of the legislature "to report on the utility of a machine called the Columbia Spinster, so as to entitle, in case the same be approved, the inventor of the same to the sum provided by law for his benefit."[14]

The account books and records of this period show that the planters often employed their poorer white neighbors at spinning and weaving cloth. They also built loom houses and trained their slaves in the household arts. Some idea of the extent of the homespun industry in the South may be obtained from the census of 1910 which reports that 7,376,154, 3,083,188, and 3,688,534 yards of cotton goods were made by families and small concerns during the previous year in North Carolina, South Carolina and Georgia, respectively. The estimated value of these goods in North Carolina was $2,989,140, in South Carolina $1,541,594, and in Georgia $1,797,264.[15]

The possibilities of expanding cotton manufacturing were noted by a reporter in 1810 when he wrote in part:

> The water spinners of cotton, in one of the states, have represented to its marshal, that they can make eighty-two pounds and one half of yarn by each spindle in every year.

[12] *Ibid.*, pp. 535-536; W. R. Bagnall, *The Textile Industries of the United States*, Vol. I, pp. 368, 373.
[13] M. T. Copeland, *The Cotton Manufacturing Industry of the United States*, p. 4.
[14] August Kohn, *The Cotton Mills of South Carolina*, p. 11.
[15] *U. S. Census, 1910*, pp. 130, 144, 148.

But the owners of other spinning mills deem it unsafe to calculate upon more than fifty-two pounds of yarn per annum for each spindle. The quality of the yarn under consideration is said to be suitable for cotton cloth, of twenty-seven inches in width, worth 40 cents per yard. At the lowest of the rates the United States, had they 1,160,000 spindles, could work up into yarn the sixty-four millions of pounds weight of cotton, which are the *maximum* of our exportation, in any one year. In a proportion, . . . this number of spindles would require a capital of nearly 70,000,000 dollars. . . . Sixth-four millions of pounds of cotton . . . would produce about 50,000,000 of pounds of cotton yarn and with the labor . . . of about 58,000 persons . . . , one eighth ought to be adult males. The remaining seven eighths, might be women and children. This employment of less than *an hundredth part* of our white population . . . would be no inconvenience to agriculture or commerce. . . .

The yarn, thus manufactured . . . would amount to fifty millions of dollars; a sum exceeding the aggregate value of all the exports of *American* articles. . . .

But, if the weaving of this be executed, as may be done with perfect ease, by the employment of 100,000 women (less than one sixth of our adult females) with *the fly shuttle* during *one half* of each working day in the year, the quantity of cloth . . . would amount to about 200,000,000 of yards. This quantity of cloth, at one third of a dollar per yard, would be worth about 67,000,000 dollars.[16]

The advantages and disadvantages of manufacturing versus the exportation of raw cotton were debated throughout the South. Men like John Randolph and Langdon Cleves were opposed to the establishment of mills, whereas John C. Calhoun contended: "It is better for us that our cotton go out in yarn and goods than in the raw state." The ideas expressed by the editor of the paper at Athens, Georgia, concerning the establishment of a mill in that vicinity are, therefore, significant.

A sense of safety and a feeling of indepenence combined, doubtless, with an expectation of profit have urged gentlemen to an undertaking against which their political connections are at war. And we are authorized to state that these sentiments have by no means undergone a change; that their project is certainly not to give countenance to a system which they have always denounced but it is to be regarded as a measure unquestionably defensive.[17]

---

16 Tench Coxe, "A Statement of the Arts and Manufacturer of the U.S.A. in the Year 1810," *U. S. Census, 1810* (1814), p. x.
17 J. L. Watkins, *King Cotton*, p. 101.

4

For the next several decades, however, only a few cotton mills were established in the South. The first one built in Georgia, in 1810, was situated on Upton Creek, nine miles southeast of Washington in Wilkes County, and was a brown stone, 40 by 60 foot, two-story structure.[18] Shortly thereafter the first mill built in Georgia run by means other than horse power was constructed near Athens.

There were two mills in North Carolina before 1820, one near Lincolnton and the other on the Tar River in Edgecombe County. The latter mill was burned by Yankee troopers during the Civil War but was later rebuilt and continues to manufacture cloth today on the original site.

Information available on the number of mills operating in New England during the early part of the 19th Century is of questionable validity, but the figures included in the following table, compiled from a report by Secretary of the Treasury McLane in 1832, is doubtless as accurate as any other tabulation.

TABLE I

COTTON MILLS ERECTED IN NEW ENGLAND BY DATE OF ESTABLISHMENT[19]

	Me.	N. H.	Vt.	Mass.	R. I.	Conn.	TOTAL
To 1805				1	1	2	4
1805				1	1		2
1806				1	1	1	3
1807					4		4
1808				1			1
1809	1			1		1	3
1810		1		3	2	2	8
1811				5	1	1	7
1812			1	9	4	3	17
1813	1			13	3	3	20
1814		3		12	4	6	25
1815		2		4	2	3	11
1816		2		1			3
1817		3			1		4
1818		1		1	1	1	4
1819			1		2		3
1820		1		4		2	7
1821		1		2		1	4
1822		1		3	1	2	7
1823	1	2		4	5	7	19
1824		4	1	2	4	5	16

[18] *Ibid.*, p. 99.
[19] Clive Day, "The Early Development of the American Cotton Manufacture," *Quarterly Journal of Economics*, Vol. 39 (1935), p. 452.

	Me.	N. H.	Vt.	Mass.	R. I.	Conn.	TOTAL
1825	----	1	----	8	2	6	17
1826	----	1	----	7	6	2	16
1827	----	1	1	4	5	4	15
1828	----	7	1	7	3	13	31
1829	----	3	----	6	2	5	16
1830	----	2	----	3	7	4	16
1831	----	4	3	10	8	6	31
1832	2	----	----	4	----	7	13
Total Dated	5	40	8	117	70	87	327
Total Undated	1	2	2	75	49	14	146
Total Enumerated	6	42	10	102	119	101	470

Except for Massachusetts there is no great difference in the number of mills listed above and those noted in a survey of New England cotton mills by the Friends of Domestic Industry. This organization reported that in 1831 Maine had 8, New Hampshire 40, Vermont 17, Massachusetts 250, Rhode Island 116, and Connecticut 94 cotton mills, for a total of 525.[20]

The statistics on the number of spindles in operation during the early 1800's are not very reliable, but in a report to Congress the following figures were given.[21]

NUMBER OF SPINDLES IN THE UNITED STATES

1805	4,500
1807	8,000
1809	31,000
1810	87,000
1815	130,000
1820	220,000
1825	800,000

It may be noted that the number of spindles in operation increased rapidly after 1807 and the vast majority of the 800,000 spindles in 1825 were located in New England with only a few in operation in the South or West.

During this period cotton mills began operation in the Piedmont section. It was necessary, however, to transport the textile machinery from Charleston over unimproved roads for more than two hundred miles to establish these mills.[22]

The problems of establishing mills in the interior of Georgia were many. For example, John Shly took six weeks of constant travel in

[20] Friends of Domestic Industry, *Report of Committees*, Convention at New York, Oct. 26, 1831, p. 112.
[21] 24th Cong., 1st Sess., Ex. Doc., No. 146, p. 5.
[22] See J. B. O. Landrum, *History of Spartanburg County.*

6

the Alligator line stage coaches to journey from his home in Georgia to Pennsylvania where he bought the first machinery for making cotton bagging ever brought to Georgia. The machinery was brought by boat to Savannah and then by wagon for two hundred miles to Reedy Creek in Jefferson County. This mill, when completed, was equipped with four looms which made between 300 and 400 yards of cotton bagging per day, and the product was sold to planters who made cotton containers or bales with it.[23]

The problem of transportation facilities likewise restricted the development of mills in North Carolina where water power fed small streams leading to a difficult coast. There was no navigation and over-land communication was difficult.

By 1830, because of the sectional disagreement over the tariff question, resentment of the South over its economic dependence upon the North was common. This doubtless stimulated the movement for manufacturers and the establishment of larger and more complete factories. At this time, too, there was a more general introduction of the power loom, and an effort to complete all the processes of manufacture within one mill.[24]

It was during this period that the first cotton mill was built on the Flint River in Alabama. This manufactory, incorporated by the legislature in 1832 as the "Bell Factory of the County of Madison," was so named because in the absence of a steam whistle, a large bell was rung to summon the employees to work. It operated 3,000 spindles and 100 looms and for the next ten or fifteen years was possibly one of the two most important industrial enterprises in the state.[25]

By 1838, however, there were, according to James L. Watkins, eleven cotton mills in operation in North Carolina. Besides the two mills situated near Lincolnton and in Edgecombe County, there were two in Fayetteville, one steam power mill in Greensboro, one in Witten, one in Mocksville, two in Orange County, one in Randolph County and a steam power mill in Lexington. Seven mills were under construction in the state.[26]

In the same year an optimistic editor in North Carolina, in pointing out the advantages of abundant and cheap water supply, nearness to raw material and willing labor said: "We may venture the opinion that in two years, North Carolina will not only supply her demand for her own consumption with the coarser cotton fabrics, but will also send them out for sale into the markets of the world.

---

[23] Charles C. Jones, *Memorial History of Augusta, Georgia*, p. 397.
[24] V. S. Clark, *The South in the Building of the Nation*, Vol. V, p. 322.
[25] A. B. Moore, *History of Alabama*, pp. 283-84.
[26] J. L. Watkins, *King Cotton*, p. 58.

On the whole the manufacturers of the northern states need not much longer count North Carolina as one of their markets, they may rather regard her as a competitor, and one, who, from the great advantages she possesses, will soon become very formidable."[27]

Several decades passed, however, before this prophecy was fulfilled and in 1840 there were only 25 small mills in operation in North Carolina with a total of 47,934 spindles.[28] There were at the same time 180,927 active spindles in the South as compared with 1,597,394 spindles in the New England.[29] The total number for the nation in 1840 was 2,284,631, the capital invested in the 1240 mills amounted to $51,102,359 and the value of the products was $46,350,453.[30]

During the period from 1840 to 1860 the number of spindles in the United States more than doubled totaling slightly more than 5,235,000. The capital invested in the industry in 1860 amounted to $98,585,269 while the value of the products was $115,681,774.[31]

Of the 1091 cotton mills in the United States in 1860, 570 were located in New England. In the next twenty years the number of spindles in this area increased from 1,597,394 to 3,857,962 and the value of the products of the cotton mills grew from $46,350,453 to $115,681,744.

The South did not enjoy the great growth of the industry as did New England. While the number of establishments declined from 248 in 1840 to 165 in 1860, the number of active spindles increased from 180,927 to 298,551. During the same period the value of the product increased from $2,241,595 to $8,460,488.

But a new movement began in the South when William Gregg, a pioneer of larger industry, began to awaken the South to its advantages for cotton manufacturing. Through his writings he did much to remove the popular prejudice against industrial corporations. While expressing his ideas he also put them into practice. In 1846, at Graniteville, where water power, water navigation and railways met, he founded the South's first large mill having 8,400 spindles and 300 looms.

This structure, perhaps the most attractive of its type in the United States when completed, is in use today. It is constructed of white granite, is 350 feet long with two massive towers overlooking

[27] Reprinted by *The News and Observer*, Raleigh, N.C., Oct. 5, 1924.
[28] *U. S. Census, 1840*.
[29] *U. S. Census, 1900*, Vol. IX, Part 3, p. 54.
[30] *Ibid.*, p. 27.
[31] *Ibid.*, p. 24.

a lawn in front. During the early years fountains on the lawn spouted water fifteen feet into the air.[32]

During the Civil War a large number of mills in New England had to close due to a lack of cotton. However, during this period several new mills were built and a number of cotton manufacturers took advantage of this idle time to rebuild or enlarge their establishments. The cotton shortage was fully felt in 1863 and it is estimated that only 1,700,000 of the 4,000,000 spindles in the North were in operation at that time.[33]

Many mills in the South were destroyed during the war by Federal troops or reduced to a state of dilapidation by protracted use without repairs. The revival from the war was surprisingly quick. Graniteville and Vaucluse were spared from the matches of the raiders but came out of the war in a run down condition. Two years after the mills had been burned in Columbus, Georgia, two had been rebuilt and were making cloth.[34] In 1867, the cotton mills of Augusta, Georgia were so successful as to receive a special mention in the report of The Commission of the Paris Exposition as illustrating conditions favoring cotton manufacturing in the South.[35]

Of the 7,132,415 active spindles in the United States in 1870, 5,858,962 were located in the New England states and 327,817 in the South. At the same time, the number of looms in New England outnumbered those in the South, 114,982 to 6,256.[36]

During this period a demand arose for more mills to care for the needs of the working classes, and it was frequently proposed to build them right in the heart of the cotton fields.[37] An aid to the future industrial development was the increase in population of 1,281,944 in the four important cotton manufacturing states between 1870 and 1880. With the increasing population and with more labor available than was required to cultivate the farm land, it is not surprising that a textile industry which employed many persons prospered.[38]

In this period the South began to enjoy the benefits of recovery from the war and reconstruction periods. The establishment of responsible governments, in place of political misrule and political corruption, brought about a return in confidence which had made

---

[32] *Debow's Review,* Vol. VI, pp. 370-372.
[33] V. S. Clark, *History of Manufacturers in the United States,* Vol. II, p. 30.
[34] V. S. Clark, *The South in the Building of the Nation,* Vol. VI, p. 225.
[35] V. S. Clark, *The History of Manufactures in the United States,* Vol. II, pp. 107-8.
[36] *Census of the U. S.* (1900), Vol. IX, Part II, p. 54.
[37] Broadus Mitchell, *The Rise of the Cotton Mills in the South,* p. 140.
[38] *South Carolina State Board of Agriculture,* 1905, Manufacturers, Part II, p. 657.

possible the concentration of capital for the development of cotton manufacturing. It is, therefore, the year 1880 that such writers as M. T. Copeland, V. S. Clark and Broadus Mitchell set as the year of revival of the Southern textile industry.

It is possible, too, that the Cotton Exposition in Atlanta in 1881 gave impetus to the industry. It is reported that during this exposition the Governor of Georgia appeared on the grounds dressed in a suit of cottonade manufactured on the premises from cotton picked from boles the same day. Doubtless many manufacturers were impressed with the idea that finished cloth, as well as coarse yarns, might be produced more easily and more profitably in the South.[39] Interest in the Atlanta Exposition was apparently pronounced for, when it closed, some of the exhibits were moved to Charleston and formed the nucleus of an industrial display.[40]

Many southerners agreed with the Charleston *News and Courier* which in 1881 reported the organization of the Charleston Manufacturing Company under the caption, "The Dawn of a New Era."[41] While many investors in cotton mills had as their prime motive the aid to the city in establishing the industry, in this instance such a motive was indirect. An editorial commended the Charleston Manufacturing Company "as a means of enlarging income . . . [t]he employment given to hundreds of persons . . . will increase the value of house property at once. They who earn nothing can't spend much. It was calculated last year that every $228 invested in cotton manufactures in South Carolina supported one person. . . . It is evident that the building of half a dozen cotton factories would revolutionize Charleston. Two or three million dollars additional poured annually into the pockets of shopkeepers would make them think that the commercial millenium had come."[42]

Growth in cotton manufacturing in the South was, therefore, phenomenal between 1880 and 1890. The number of mills increased from 161 to 239 and the active spindles and looms more than tripled in number, increasing respectively from 542,048 and 11,898 to 1,554,000 and 36,266. During the same decade the industry in the New England states enjoyed somewhat less growth with their active spindles increasing in number from 8,632,087 to 10,836,155, and their looms from 184,701 to 250,116.[43]

Thus New England with 8,632,087 active spindles out of a na-

[39] P. H. Goldsmith, *The Cotton Mill South*, pp. 3-5.
[40] Broadus Mitchell, *The Rise of the Cotton Mills in the South*, pp. 124-125.
[41] *Ibid.*, p. 71.
[42] *News and Courier*, Jan. 2, 1881, cited in Mitchell, *op. cit.*, p. 132.
[43] *Census of the U. S.* (1900), Vol. IX, Part III, p. 54.

tional total of 10,653,435 was without a rival as the textile center of this country in 1890.

During the years which followed, the press urged the people to invest in cotton mills, cities bid for the enterprises with promises of exemption from taxes for a specified number of years, and railroads were often cooperative in arranging freight schedules so as to encourage southern manufacturers. High profits attracted capital from the North and numerous corporations already established increased their capital and built new mills in the South. The industry before 1900 was important enough in four states, North Carolina, South Carolina, Georgia and Alabama, to consume nearly one third of the cotton grown in those states.[44]

Great growth continued in the industry and during the decade ending in 1900 over 2,000,000 spindles and 50,000 looms were added in the New England states, while the number of spindles increased by over 2,700,000 and the looms by over 73,000 in the Southern states.[45] Approximately 67 percent of the 12,891,787 spindles in the United States in 1900 were located within thirty miles of Providence, Rhode Island, and the number of spindles in Providence County outnumbered those in any southern state except South Carolina.[46]

To speed the construction of cotton mills in the South installment plans for the purchase of stock were developed. Under such circumstances the subscription to shares, usually $100 par value, was made payable in weekly installments of 50 cents to $1 a share, without interest. Occasionally a mill was built with a 25-cent installment. Purchasers paying cash for stock were allowed a discount of about $10 on a $100 share.[47] On the other hand, some mills were controlled by one family.

A view of the unusual growth in the industry was given by August Kohn in 1903:

> The eyes of the world are upon South Carolina. It is making most rapid agricultural, industrial and educational strides. Perhaps most remarkable of all the development has been out of the cotton mill industry. It has been the wonder and the admiration of all. Twenty years ago the total capital in all textile enterprises in the State aggregated only $2,500,000. Today there are more than $35,000,000 invested in the cotton mills of this common-

---

[44] *Ibid.*, p. 29.
[45] *Ibid.*, p. 54.
[46] *Ibid.*, p. 30.
[47] Holland Thompson, *From the Cotton Field to the Cotton Mill*, pp. 82-83.

11

wealth. Think of it that the cotton mills alone represent over ten percent of the total taxable property of the State.[48]

Expansion continued in the cotton industry and by 1919 there were 33,718,953 spindles in the United States of which 17,542,926 were located in the New England states and 14,568,272 in the cotton growing states.[49] This growth continued until 1923 when 35,849,000 spindles were in operation in this country.

It was not until 1925, however, that the South surpassed New England in number of spindles in operation. Since the all time high was established in 1924 there has been a decline in the total number of active spindles in the United States. As the industry declined in New England, it became more important in the southern states. In July, 1962, there were 16,774,000 spindles active on cotton, 1,157,000 on synthetics, and 833,000 on other fibers and blends. Of this total number 17,815,000 spindles were in operation in cotton producing states with 949,000 in the other states of the Union.[50]

The following table shows the trend by years in the number of spindles and the number of bales of cotton consumed.

TABLE II

UNITED STATES
NUMBER OF SPINDLES AND NUMBER OF BALES OF COTTON CONSUMED[51]
By Years

Year	Number of Spindles[52]	Number of Bales Consumed[53]
1840	2,248,631	----------
1850	----------	641,240
1860	5,235,727	----------
1870	7,132,415	----------
1880	10,653,000	1,570,344
1890	14,188,108	2,261,600
1900	19,008,352	3,639,495
1904	23,155,613	3,749,765

[48] August Kohn, "Lead States in Cloth Making," *South Carolina Handbook*, pp. 57-58.
[49] *Census of U. S.*, (1920), Vol. X, p. 176.
[50] *Stat. Abstract of the U.S.*, 1963, p. 799.
[51] The data for the period 1840-1919 were obtained from *U. S. Census*, 1890, 1900, and 1920. For the years 1920-1962, see *Stat. Abstract of the U. S.*, 1931 and 1963.
[52] Prior to 1950, represents all spindles in place used exclusively for spinning cotton; thereafter represents all spindles in place regardless of fiber spun. On July 31, 1962, there were 16,770,000 spindles active in cotton, 1,157,000 on synthetics, 833,000 on other fibers and blends, and 727,000 idle.
[53] Excluding linters from 1920 to 1962.

Year	Number of Spindles	Number of Bales Consumed
1909	27,395,800	4,828,736
1914	30,815,731	5,167,975
1919	33,718,953	5,529,422
1920	35,481,000	6,420,000
1921	36,047,000	4,893,000
1923	36,260,000	6,666,000
1925	35,032,000	6,193,000
1927	34,410,000	7,190,000
1929	32,417,000	7,091,000
1930	31,045,000	6,106,000
1935	26,701,000	5,361,000
1940	23,586,000	7,784,000
1945	22,675,000	9,568,000
1950	21,790,000	8,851,000
1955	20,516,000	8,841,000
1960	19,222,000	9,016,000
1961	18,956,000	8,252,000
1962	18,764,000	9,071,000
1963	18,634,000	8,391,000
1964	18,446,000	8,554,000

CHAPTER II

Villages

During the industrial expansion in England the cotton mills were built at places where water power was available. Then, because of lack of adequate transportation facilities, it was necessary for many mills to construct houses for operatives in order to be assured of a sufficient number of workers to operate the mill. Some idea of the problems which confronted early mill owners in England may be had from a letter written by Samuel Greg to a friend in January, 1835[1] which explained how he bought an old mill, with a worn-out water wheel and nearly 50 cottages in 1832. An effort was made to find respectable families "who would make themselves a home and lose the migratory spirit which is one of the peculiar characteristics of the manufacturing population." The management gave them small garden plots, established a Sunday school and a playground, and instituted drawing, singing, geography and natural history classes. Evening parties were sponsored during the winter to which, as Mr. Greg expressed it, "the tolerable respectable especially those who attended Sunday School" were invited.

The management was somewhat proud of the seven warm baths installed in a small room back of the mill. Cold water was piped from a cistern above the engine house while hot water was piped in from a large tub which received waste steam from a dressing room. Men and women bathed on alternate days and paid a penny each for a bath, but a subscription of a shilling a month entitled the subscriber to a maximum of five baths a week. Mr. Greg thus felt that he had obtained a fixed and settled population from which he could obtain his workers and that the added activities made work in the mill more pleasant and life in the community more attractive.

The mill villages in England disappeared during the past century as the area became more heavily populated, and today only a few houses are owned by cotton mills.

New England

With the erection of cotton mills in New England there was, of course, the need to recruit laborers. It was necessary, therefore, to

---

[1] Samuel Greg, *Layman's Legacy*, Appendix A, pp. 315-325.

construct houses for families and boarding houses for the unmarried female workers. Sleeping rooms were occupied by 2, 4 or 6 persons. The boarders were closely chaperoned by the matrons, and the owners insisted on having strictly reputable communities. Thus they gained the confidence of the rural population and stilled the objections to their daughters going to manufacturing towns.[2] The houses closed at 10 p. m. and church attendance on Sunday was mandatory. This puritanical atmosphere not only made the areas decent but also peaceful and sober.[3]

The rents were low in the boarding houses, costing about 1/3 to 1/2 as much as in similar houses owned by private individuals in the cities. In a number of mills, however, foreigners were employed and they were not considered desirable roommates or housemates. As difficulties mounted, the houses were sold to private operators of boarding houses and the rates went up.[4]

Numerous mills in New England disposed of their houses at auction sales. This meant, of course, that employees might be outbidden and ownership go to people of other industries. In other instances financing was arranged by employers to assist operatives in purchasing the houses. As mill housing declined in the larger centers, private capital built tenements to meet the housing needs of the people. However, at the beginning of this century these housing projects had declined and slum conditions developed.[5]

The cotton mill village, which disappeared in New England during the earlier part of this century, met many of the needs of the workers during the nineteenth century. It may be noted in addition to what has already been mentioned, that mill corporations, according to H. C. Meserve, founded the first hospital in 1841. The first brick sidewalk in Lowell was in front of the boarding houses and across the yards from the mills. Running water was furnished in mills and in factory tenements in advance of public water works in New England. The first use of steam heat was in the cotton mills. The first sewage system in New England was installed when Lowell Mills provided sewers to carry away waste water from bleacheries and dye houses. Various mills had gas works before they were acquired by towns, and some were pioneers in establishing Americanization classes.[6]

---

[2] D. L. Cohn, *The Life and Times of King Cotton*, p. 196.
[3] See Vera Schlakman, *Economic History of a Factory Town*, Smith College Studies in History, Vol. XX, pp. 51-52.
[4] H. C. Meserve, *Lowell—An Industrial Dream Come True*, p. 61.
[5] Harriet L. Herring, *Passing of the Mill Village*, p. 105.
[6] See H. C. Meserve, *Lowell—An Industrial Dream Come True*, p. 61 ff.

William Gregg is credited with establishing at Graniteville, South Carolina, the first mill village in the South. In 1849 this village covered about 150 acres, contained two Gothic churches, an academy, a hotel and stores, and about 100 cottages belonging to the company and occupied by operatives. The houses varied in size from three to nine rooms each, nearly all built on the Gothic cottage order.[7] William Gregg said in referring to this community:

> We may really regard ourselves as the pioneers in developing the real character of the poor people in South Carolina. Graniteville is truly the home of the poor widow and helpless children, or for a family brought to ruin by a drunken, worthless father. Here they meet with protection, are educated free of charge, and brought to habits of industry under the care of intelligent men. The population of Graniteville is made up mainly from the poor of Edgefield, Barnwell and Lexington districts. From extreme poverty and want they have become a thrifty, happy and contended people. When they were first brought together the seventy-nine out of a hundred grown girls who could neither read nor write were a by-word around the country; that reproach has long since been removed.[8]

As in New England, the moral and the mental culture of the families also received attention in Graniteville. The use of alcohol was not permitted in the place. Young people, particularly males, were not allowed to remain in the village in idleness, and good moral character was necessary to continued residence.

During the same period somewhat similar requirements were established for residence in the De Kalb Mill village in South Carolina. A good moral character was insisted upon, children were required to attend school, and Sunday School and church attendance was encouraged. One writer thought that this village could compare in point of morals and good order with any of its size in the United States.[9]

The ideas of Gregg appealed to other cotton mill executives of the early period and bore fruit during later generations. Few urban centers were available as sites for the establishment of cotton mills where labor supply could be obtained. By necessity, therefore, the manufacturers established their mills where water power was available and built villages around them for the housing and accommo-

---

[7] See letter from William Gregg to Freeman Hunt, Oct. 22, 1849, in *Hunt's Merchant's Magazine*, Vol. 21, No. 6, pp. 671-672.
[8] August Kohn, *The Cotton Mills of South Carolina*, p. 21.
[9] Charles T. Jones, "Southern Manufacture and Internal Improvements," *De Bows Review*, Oct. 1949, p. 373.

dations of their employees. The cotton mill village was thus established as a social and economic necessity and not as a paternalistic intention on the part of the manufacturers.

During the early part of this century various mill managements endeavored to out do each other in the development of their villages. New schools, churches, stores and recreational centers were built and numerous community activities were introduced. Some mills established hospitals, and beautification of the villages was promoted by mill owners.

Housing in the Southern as in the New England mills was heavily subsidized, the operatives paying from one-third to one-half as much rent as they would have to pay for similar homes under non-mill ownership. This subsidy placed a financial burden on the owners; and so, beginning about three or four decades ago, the management of various mills sought ways to dispose of their villages. While the villages were financial liabilities, additional reasons were given for selling the houses. Some owners felt that, through home ownership, better citizenship would be developed and that the operatives, as owners of their homes, not only would take considerable pride in possession, but would assume definite roles in the community. It was believed that operatives' interest in civic affairs would increase as they became taxpayers and that better results would be obtained from their general participation in the affairs of local government.

Home ownership promotes stability, for in ordinary times a man's home ties him to a community. Sometimes this has been distasteful to the cotton mill operative, however, who as a renter enjoys mobility, and who prefers something of the life of a nomad.

With the sale of the villages, the mill owners were taken out of the real estate business and thus were relieved of the worries associated with the enterprise. The management then could concentrate more on manufacturing, which is its real interest in the business world. Numerous executives have expressed relief at being rid of various community problems which they had to solve prior to selling their villages.

Executives have pointed to the new social conditions and the changes in industrial relations which they feel lend support to the sale of the houses to operatives. Since the employees enjoyed greater incomes, home ownership was not only possible but desirable, giving economic security as well as social recognition to the workers.

On the other hand, certain operators felt that home ownership increased the responsibility of the workers, for since they are finan-

17

cially involved in the community, their interest in the welfare and progress of the mills is correspondingly increased.

The procedure followed in the sale of homes to the operatives in the cotton mill villages was, in general, the same. The announcements of the sales were made some months in advance so that the operatives could prepare to meet the purchase requirements. Outside men, usually from realty companies, were requested to survey the villages and set the sale price for the dwellings, taking into consideration the locations, condition of the properties and sizes of the houses. Some appraisals were made at about 90 per cent of the market value of the property. Some mills financed the sales and required no down payment, while others requested 5 per cent of the assessed valuation. A ten per cent down payment was commonly charged, but in many instances the down payment was scattered over a number of months. When building and loan associations handled the financing, down payments, of course, were required, and the interest charged ranged from 6 to 7 per cent per annum on the loans. Charges by mill managements on the same type of loans were from 4 to 6 per cent. The loans usually extended over a 10 to 12 year period. Operatives living in the houses were given first refusal. If persons living in the houses did not desire to purchase them, other employees of the mill were given the opportunity to buy the dwellings.

Because of the liberal appraisals of the houses and the general increase in the value of real estate, numerous operatives have realized substantial profits on the sales of their property and there have been very few foreclosures on dwellings.

The trend in the sale of mill villages which commenced about 30 years ago in the South went into full stride after World War II. Today few such villages remain. All the executives of mills where villages have been sold who were interviewed during the course of this study stated that they thought the sales were to the mutual advantage of the employers and employees. Some mills have retained a few houses for key personnel while others continue ownership of those near the mill to allow for future expansion, should such seem feasible.

In the sale of the houses in the cities or towns the change-over was rather simple. In the smaller areas, however, mills often continued to care for such things as, for example, the water supply, collection of garbage and fire protection.[10]

---

[10] Harriet L. Herring, *Passing of the Mill Village*, pp. 43-49.

Some mills continue their recreational programs and have even enlarged them after having sold their villages.

The Leroy Springs and Company, chartered in 1938, has charge of the recreational program in all the communities in which the Springs Cotton Mills are located. By 1963, this company had over $2,000,000 invested in property and equipment devoted to recreation. Two major facilities are Springs Park on the Catawba River in Lancaster County and Springmaid Beach near Myrtle Beach, South Carolina. The company also owns golf courses (36 holes), 32 lanes of bowling, four swimming pools, four softball fields, five tennis courts, four community centers, four youth and teenage centers and six playgrounds.[11]

The Callaway Mills sold their villages in the 1940's, but at present the Callaway Foundation is financing an extensive community development program. In June, 1964, a new $600,000 educational center was opened in Manchester, Georgia, which, like the one already in use in LaGrange, includes an excellent gymnasium for basketball games, a swimming pool, and facilities for other athletic and social activities. The Coleman Library, constructed in 1955, has a circulation of over 12,000 books a year, thus assisting in the cultural development of the LaGrange community.

The Callaway Foundation makes monthly contributions, based on membership, to the churches located in the former villages of Callaway Mills. On major church improvement projects it pays one-half the cost of such improvements when completed, and the churches pay the other half of the costs.

Included among the few villages still owned by the mills is the one established at Graniteville in 1845. This village presently contains 299 houses, averaging five rooms and all have running water and bathrooms. The average rental charge is $1.06 per room per week.

In 1950 the Gregg Park Civic Center was established and a recreation center built. The center is available to all employees and the residents of the villages of Graniteville. A staff of five members supervises the activities of the center.

The largest and best known mill village in existence today is the unincorporated town of Kannapolis, North Carolina. Certain streets are kept up by the state, others by the Cannon Mills. Policing of the area is by county policemen and the water supply and sewage disposal are cared for by the mill. The equipment for the volunteer

---

[11] See *America's Textile Reporter*, Oct. 10, 1963, pp. 90-94.

fire department is owned by the mill and the mill employs persons to maintain the stations.

The houses have running water and bathrooms and are equipped with water heaters. They rent for $1.25 a week per room, and 50 cents a week for a small garage or $1 for a large one. While a number of houses have been added since World War II, none have been built during the past decade. The houses are maintained and the garbage collected by the mill with no charges made for either of the services.

A Young Men's Christian Association was organized in this community in 1908, and, after occupying various buildings, was finally housed in 1939 in an imposing building costing approximately $500,000. There are presently over 11,000 members of the Y.M.C.A., about 4,000 of whom are women and girls. The membership fees are $2 for adults and $1 a year for children under 16 years of age. Housed in this building is a library of about 16,000 books which, during the first six months of 1964, had a total circulation of 19,445 books. There are two regulation size gymnasiums marked for basketball, volleyball, badminton and indoor softball. Both are used interchangeably by men and women.

The Y.M.C.A. contains club rooms for both sexes, and it is possible to serve 1500 persons at dinner by combining rooms. Over 15,000 meals were served to groups during the first half year of 1964. The facilities of a health room are available to members of the Health Club who have paid an additional fee. Members of the Y.M.C.A. may enjoy the use of the bowling alleys for 25 cents a game, and for the same sum play pool for an hour. A swimming pool is also available to members.

The physical education department has organized gym classes and numerous athletic teams for men and boys. Bowling, basketball, baseball and other leagues have been established and numerous athletic clubs organized which are composed of various age groups.

The Y.M.C.A. operates a day camp for boys and girls in addition to Camp Elliott near Black Mountain, North Carolina. A $30 charge is made for a two week stay at Camp Elliott. Various activities on numerous play grounds and softball fields in Kannapolis are directed by the Y.M.C.A.

The Y.M.C.A. with its 27 full-time and 10 to 12 part-time employees receives liberal support from the Cannon Mills which also makes contributions from time to time to various churches in the community.

Numerous private business establishments, including a number of chain stores, operate in the business section of Kannapolis.

In general, however, the mill villages in the South have practically disappeared although, as in England and New England, they served a good purpose in their time. Economic development and improved public and private transportation facilities have brought about a changed way of life which made for the passing of the mill village.

CHAPTER III

TARIFF

Early in American history the Congress of the United States felt disposed to place a tax on cotton goods imported into this country. Thus, in March, 1791, a law was enacted which provided that a duty of 7.5 per cent ad valorem be laid on manufacturers of cotton brought into the United States.[1] The act of 1794 provided for a 5 per cent ad valorem tax, and the act of 1804 exempted from duty, among other commodities, rags of cotton.[2]

The rapid growth in the number of spindles in operation before and during the War of 1812 stopped when peace was made in 1815. Foreign imports took a large part of the market and many mills closed. Assistance was sought from Congress and the Act of 1816 was passed. This Act provided for a duty of 25 per cent ad valorem for three years, at the end of which time the duty would be 20 per cent under certain conditions. The Act further provided that cloths costing less than 25 cents a square yard (for the purpose of determining the duty to be charged) and also unbleached and uncolored cotton twist and all bleached or colored yarn which cost less than 60 and 75 cents per pound, respectively, should be deemed to have cost 60 or 75 cents per pound, and duty thereon be charged accordingly.[3]

During the decade following the passage of the Act of 1816, the price on cotton declined thus making the minimum duty proportionally greater. The importation of certain kinds of cotton cloths, therefore, was no longer profitable. The fall in price brought financial problems to some manufacturers, and additional protection was sought. Accordingly, the Act of 1824 raised the minimum valuation to 30 cents per square yard. This minimum was increased 5 cents per square yard in 1828.[4]

The Act of 1842 provided, with a few exceptions, for a 30 per cent ad valorem duty on all manufactures of cotton and goods in which cotton was a component part.[5] Some changes, however, were made by the Act of 1861 where various categories of cloth were

---

[1] *Tariff Acts, 1789-1909*, Doc. No. 671, 61 Cong. 2nd Sess., p. 19.
[2] *Ibid.*, p. 49.
[3] *Ibid.*, p. 58.
[4] *Ibid.*, p. 88.
[5] *Ibid.*, p. 121.

established with duty levied from one to four cents per square yard. The Act provided for an additional charge of one-half of one cent if the cloth was bleached; and cloth printed, colored or stained was subject to an additional 10 per cent tax.

During the war period the price of cotton, of course, increased as also did the duty on cloth, as provided for by the Act of 1864. In addition to a tax ranging from five to seven and one-half cents per square yard was a twenty to thirty-five per cent ad valorem tax, depending upon the classification of the cloth.[6]

The Act of 1872 provided for a 10 per cent reduction in duties imposed upon all manufactures of cotton of which cotton is the component part of chief value. Later, in 1883, the duty of common grades of goods was reduced to 25 cents. However, while the duty on this type of cloth, which could be produced competitively in this country, was reduced, it was increased on other grades. For example, the duty on cotton laces, embroideries and trimmings, which had been 35 per cent, was increased to 40 per cent ad valorem. On such garments as stockings, shirts, hose, webbing, cotton cords and braids, a 35 per cent ad valorem tax was levied.[7]

Legislation passed by Congress in 1890 both raised and lowered rates. The duty on a cheap grade of unbleached cotton was reduced from 2.5 to 2 cents a yard, but on the highest grade of cotton prints the duty was increased from 6 to 6.75 cents a yard. On various cotton materials the duty ranged from 35 to 50 per cent ad valorem.[8]

The Wilson Act of 1894 reduced the specific duties for the heavier fabrics, but the tax on the finer grades remained about the same as they were in 1890. The ad valorem rates on the better materials were reduced by about 10 per cent. It is estimated, however, that the average duty collected in 1895 on all cotton cloth was about 41 per cent.[9]

The Act of 1897 left unchanged the duty on cloth containing less than 200 threads to the square inch. Specific duties on heavier cloth were about one cent higher than they were in 1894. Especially heavy rates were established on cotton stockings, velvets, corduroys and other materials by combining specific and ad valorem duties. Cotton wares not otherwise provided for enjoyed a 5 per cent cut in duty from 50 per cent in 1890 to 45 per cent in 1897.[10]

---

[6] *Ibid.*, pp. 238-39.
[7] *Ibid.*, pp. 334-35.
[8] *Ibid.*, pp. 394-95.
[9] M. T. Copeland, *The Cotton Manufacturing Industry of the United States*, p. 242.
[10] *Tariff Acts*, 1789-1909, Doc. 671, 61 Cong. 2nd Sess., pp. 570-75.

The tariff act of 1909 brought both increases and decreases in duties. There was, for example, a reduction in the duty on the coarser varieties of grey corded yarn and a 10 per cent reduction on card laps, sliver and roving.

The duties on cotton were based on the number of threads per square inch. Six classes were established, and each class was subdivided into grey, bleached and colored cloth; each subdivision was graded according to weight or value, or both. The ad valorem tax in each class was increased. The duty of an extra cent per yard was placed on mercerized cotton.

Advances in the duties on hosiery were made in the Act of 1909. On one class there was a duty of 70 cents per dozen plus 15 per cent, which amounted to at least 88 per cent, as compared with 68 per cent under the Act of 1897. On the second-class hosiery (valued at from $1 to $1.50 per dozen pairs), the duty was raised from 60 cents plus 15 per cent, to 85 cents plus 15 per cent, and on the third class (valued at from $1.50 to $2 per dozen pairs), from 70 cents plus 15 per cent, to 90 cents plus 15 per cent.

Generally speaking, the reductions in duties on cheaper cotton goods were of little importance while duties on the higher priced goods were raised 5 to 10 per cent and the duties on cheaper cotton hosiery about 20 per cent.[11]

The Act of 1913 reduced duties on a number of items. For example, the rate was reduced on cotton material with counts from number 9 to 19, 7½ per cent ad valorem; from number 20 to 39, 10 per cent ad valorem; from 40 to 49, 15 per cent ad valorem. The rates rose progressively to 25 per cent on yarns and to 27½ per cent on plain cloths. A 30 per cent duty was placed on bleached, dyed, printed or mercerized cloth. On ordinary stockings the rate was 20 per cent, but on fashioned hosiery the rates were higher—30 per cent if not valued at more than 70 cents per dozen pairs, 40 per cent if not valued at more than $1.20 per dozen pairs, and 50 per cent if the value exceeds $1.20. Cotton knit goods and wearing apparel were taxed at 30 per cent ad valorem.[12]

The Act of 1922, like the Act of 1913, provided for ad valorem rates on a progressive scale. The rates ranged from 5 per cent on the coarsest yarns to 45 per cent on the finest cloth; but in no case should the duties exceed 45 per cent ad valorem on cotton cloth.[13] Knit goods and wearing apparel were limited to a 45 and 35 per

---

[11] *Ibid.*, pp. 730-737; M. T. Copeland, "Duties on Cotton Goods in the Tariff Act of 1910," *Quart. Journ. of Econ.*, Vol. XXIV, pp. 422-428.
[12] U. S. Tariff Com., *Comparison of Tariff Acts, 1909, 1913, 1922*, pp. 150-68.
[13] *Ibid.*, p. 160.

cent ad valorem tax. The duty on fashioned hose was set 50 per cent ad valorem.

The general arrangement of duties established in 1922 was retained in the 1930 Act but at somewhat higher levels. For example, the duties on tapestries and other Jacquard-Figured upholstery cloths was increased from 45 to 55 per cent and on cloth containing wool from 40 to 60 per cent. On finer goods the increase in duties ranged from 17 to 22 per cent ad valorem.[14] Generally speaking the Tariff Act of 1930 provided higher rates for the higher priced than for the lower priced cloths on the assumption that the difference between domestic and foreign costs was greater for the higher priced goods because a larger proportion of their cost consisted of labor.

The situation changed, however, when Japan began to put medium and low priced goods on the markets of the world, since wages were lower there than in America or in European countries. This problem was cared for by the President acting under authority vested in him by the Act of 1930 which empowered him after an investigation of the Commission to proclaim changes in rates of duty if he thought necessary to equalize differences in costs of production.[15] The Trade Agreements Act of 1934 also made possible changes in tariff rates and many modifications in duties were made during the 1930's and 1940's.[16]

General Agreement on Tariffs and Trade

While reductions in tariffs had been realized under the Reciprocal Trade Agreements Act of 1934, the United States government felt the necessity for additional reductions in trade barriers. Therefore, in 1947, the United States invited twenty-three nations to negotiate reciprocal trade agreements with it, and among themselves, at Geneva. At this meeting the General Agreement on Tariffs and Trade was created which, among other things, established rules concerning imposition of internal duties and trade restrictions, import quotas and operation of exchange control.

The increase in imports, especially fabrics, led to the negotiation in 1959 between the United States and Japan of a quota system covering all categories of cotton textile exports from Japan to the United States. This "voluntary" agreement provided for a quota of 225 million square yards of cotton fabric, both in the form of yard goods and some types of makeup goods. Italy, an important source

---

[14] U. S. Tariff Com., *Comparison of Tariff Acts, 1922-1930*, pp. 92-100.
[15] *U. S. State at Large*, Vol. XLVI, Sec. 336, p. 701.
[16] See U. S. Tariff Com., *Summaries of Tariff Information*, Vol. IX.

of velveteen, voluntarily limited its exports of the fabric to the United States to about 1.4 million yards.[17]

While the voluntary quotas imposed on Japan and Italy limited the flow of cotton fabrics from these countries to the United States, imports continued to rise from such other countries as Hong Kong, India, Portugal, Spain and Pakistan. It was, therefore, obvious that the bilateral agreements were not effective in lowering textile imports into the United States.

Problems concerning the textile industry became more serious. A favorable balance of trade in textiles in 1950 of $183,000,000 had by 1960 deteriorated to an unfavorable balance of trade of $374,000,000. Numerous textile mills had closed and profits were low. These problems demanded attention, so on May 2, 1961, President Kennedy presented a seven-point program concerning the textile industry.

Point six, dealing with foreign trade, read as follows:

". . . have directed the Department of State to arrange for calling an early conference of the principal textile exporting and importing countries. This conference will seek international understanding which will provide a basis for trade and will avoid undue disruption of established industries."

The conference of sixteen important importing and exporting countries met in July, 1961, and adopted the International Textile Agreement, known as the short-term arrangement for a twelve-month period, beginning October 1, 1961.

Under this agreement the contracting countries agreed to deal with immediate problems relating to cotton textiles through international action designed (1) to increase significantly access to markets where imports are at present subject to restriction; (2) to maintain orderly access to markets where restrictions are not at present maintained; and (3) to secure from exporting countries— where necessary—a measure of restraint in their export policy to avoid disruptive effects in import markets.[18]

By terms of the arrangement, a participating country could request any other participating country to restrain imports if unrestricted imports of cotton textiles were causing, or threatening to cause, disruption in its domestic market. Imports were not to be cut below the level of the twelve-month period ending June 30, 1961, and the agreement covered 64 categories of cotton textile products. Restriction of imports by category of product was specified.

---

[17] *Problems of the Textile Industry*, Second Supp., Rept. of Com. on Com., U. S. Senate, 87th Cong., 2nd Sess. Rept. No. 1314, p. 2.
[18] *Ibid.*, p. 9.

A country requested to restrain its exports to a stated level was permitted to exceed that level for any category by five per cent, provided its total exports to the requesting country did not exceed the aggregate for all categories.

The participating countries also agreed to take action to "prevent circumvention or frustration of the short-term arrangement by non-participants, or by transhipment, or by substitution of directly competitive textiles."

The agreement further held that, "It is intended by the participating countries that this procedure will be used sparingly, with full regard for their agreed objective of attaining and safeguarding maximum freedom of trade, and only to avoid disruption of domestic industry resulting from an abnormal increase in imports."

The criteria for the determination of "market disruption" was (1) a sharp and substantial increase of imports of particular products from particular sources; (2) the products must be offered at prices which are substantially below those prevailing for similar goods of comparable quality in the market of the importing country; (3) there must be serious damage or threat of serious damage to domestic producers; (4) the price differentials must not arise from governmental intervention in the fixing or formation of prices or from dumping practices.

Under provisions of this agreement the United States banned imports of eight categories of cotton textiles from Hong Kong, effective March 3, 1962.

Shortly after the Geneva meeting in 1961, the United States concluded a new bilateral agreement with Japan to be effective during the year 1962. Japan agreed to an overall limit of exports to the United States for 1962 of 275 million square yards. It was specified that about 46 per cent of this amount was to be in the form of cotton cloth, 36 per cent woven apparel, and the remaining 21 per cent in the form of made-up goods, knit goods and miscellaneous cotton textiles. It was also agreed if, as a result of these ceilings, Japan felt that a third country was afforded an inequitable opportunity to increase exports of cotton textiles to the United States, the United Staes Government would take appropriate action.

The United States-Japanese agreement further provided that, should excessive concentration of cotton textile exports in any particular items (except those for which specific ceilings were established) cause or threaten disruption of the United States market, the United States Government could call for consultation with the Japanese Government to determine the appropriate course of action. Pending agreement on further action the Japanese Government

27

agreed to hold exports of the items in question at 110 per cent of the level reached during the twelve months prior to consultation.

To care for certain problems of the cotton industry after the expiration of the short term cotton textile agreement, the Cotton Textile Committee of the General Agreement on Tariffs and Trade negotiated at Geneva, Switzerland, the Long-Term Cotton Textile Arrangement on February 9, 1962. This agreement became effective October 1, 1962, and was to remain in force for five years. By October 1, 1962, the United States, Belgium, Canada, Denmark, France, Federal Republic of Germany, India, Israel, Italy, Japan, Luxembourg, Netherlands, Norway, Pakistan, Portugal, Spain, Sweden, United Arab Republic and the Kingdom of Great Britain and Northern Ireland accepted or acceded to the long-term arrangements.

The new agreement is similar to the short-term arrangement. Both contain provisions to avoid circumvention of the agreement by trans-shipment or re-routing substitution of competitive textiles and action by nonparticipants.

Under this agreement importing nations threatened by or subjected to market disruption on any category of cotton textiles can freeze imports for one year to the level of the first twelve of the preceding fifteen months. If these conditions continue, the freeze can be extended for another year, after which increases can be limited to five per cent a year. Decisions in such instances can be made unilaterally by the importing nations. While decisions affecting imports are made unilaterally, the Cotton Textile Committee of GATT is empowered to supervise the implementation of the agreements. This Committee, made up of representatives of the countries party to the arrangement, may also make such studies on trade in cotton textiles as participating countries may decide, may collect statistical and other information necessary for the discharge of its functions, and is empowered to request the participating countries to furnish such information.

Article 4 permits participating countries to enter into mutually acceptable agreements on other terms not inconsistent with the basic objectives of the arrangement. The contracting countries, however, must keep the Cotton Textiles Committee fully informed of such agreements which have a bearing on the operation of the Long-Term Cotton Textile Arrangement.[19]

Pursuant to Article 4 by an exchange of notes between representatives of this country and foreign countries the United States

---

[19] *U. S. Treaties and Other International Agreements,* Vol. XIII, Pt. 3, pp. 2673-97.

consummated textile agreements with China, October 19, 1963; Colombia, June 9, 1965; Greece, July 17, 1964; India, April 15, 1964; Israel, November 5 and 22, 1963; Italy, July 6, 1962; Jamaica, October 1, 1963; Japan, August 27, 1963; and August 28, 1963; Philippines, February 24, 1964; Portugal, March 12, 1964; Spain, July 16, 1963; Turkey, July 17, 1964; and United Arab Republic, December 4, 1963.

These agreements, based on discussions between representatives of the contracting countries, propose to provide for an orderly development of trade in cotton textiles between the United States and the other contracting countries. Usually the arrangements provide for limitation of imports in stated categories of cotton textiles for a designated period of time. An examination on the provisions of only two of these agreements will be made.

The agreement with Turkey entered into on July 17, 1964 listed the limitations on exports of various categories of cotton textiles to the United States for a twelve-month period beginning July 1, 1964 and provides that such may be increased by five per cent for the twelve-month period beginning July 1, 1965. At the end of each subsequent twelve-month period these limitations can be increased five per cent over the levels of the immediately preceding twelve-month period. Each government has agreed to supply data requested by the other Government and to consult on the implementation of the agreement. This agreement is to remain in force until June 30, 1967, but either Government is empowered to propose revision in its terms no later than 90 days prior to the beginning of a new twelve-month period. By written notice given 90 days prior to the beginning of a twelve-month period, either government may terminate the agreement effective at the beginning of the twelve-month period.[20]

The second, more recent agreement, resulted from bilateral talks held in Bogota between representatives of Colombia and the United States Departments of Commerce, Labor and State. It was concluded by an exchange of notes between United States Ambassador C. T. Oliver and Colombian Minister of Foreign Affairs Gernando Gomez Martinez. This agreement, effective July 1, 1965, covers 64 categories of cotton textiles and continues in force to June 30, 1969. Other features of the arrangement are: (1) During the first year of the agreement Colombia will limit its exports of cotton textiles to an aggregate of 24 million square yards equivalent and, within this limit, to the following levels: (a) yarn (categories 1-4), 12 million

---

[20] *U. S. Treaties and other International Acts*, Dept. of State, Series 5619, pp. 1-2.

square yards equivalent; (b) fabrics (categories 5-27), 11,500,000 square yards, and (c) make-up goods, apparel, and miscellaneous items (categories 28-64), 500,000 square yards. (2) Within the aggregate and group limits, the agreement also provides export ceilings for seven specific categories of cotton fabrics. (3) Colombia may exceed any of the group ceilings by five per cent so long as the aggregate volume of exports does not exceed the aggregate limit of 24 million square yards. Similarly, Colombia may exceed any of the specific category ceilings by five per cent so long as the aggregate of the exports does not exceed the applicable limits for the fabric group. (4) During the first year of the agreement only, Colombia will be entitled to export the following additional quantities to the United States: Categories 5 and 6, 1 million square yards (not more than 25 per cent shall be in category 6); category 22, 4 million square yards; and category 26, excluding duck, 2 million square yards. (5) A set of conversion factors is specified in the annex to the agreement to express various textile units in terms of square yard equivalent. (6) The two governments agreed on consultation procedures to be followed in the event of an undue concentration of Colombia's exports to the United States in categories for which the agreement provides no specific ceilings at this time. (7) The aggregate, group, and category limits and ceilings will be increased by five per cent for the second twelve-month period beginning July 1, 1966. For each subsequent year, each of the limits and ceilings will be increased by a further five per cent over those of the immediately preceding twelve-month period. (8) The Government of Colombia will endeavor to space exports evenly over each agreement year. (9) The two governments will exchange statistical information on cotton textiles as is required for the effective implementation of the agreement. (10) The export levels established by the bilateral agreement supersede the restraint actions taken by the United States Government over the past twelve months with respect to cotton textile exports from Colombia pursuant to Article 3 of the Long-Term Cotton Textile Arrangement.[21]

The loss in home markets to imported cotton textiles was not balanced by developing foreign trade. The textile industry expanded in countries which had been good markets for American goods, and numerous countries raised duties on textiles. Even without trade restrictions which limit the export of American textiles, most foreign mills have competitive advantages in lower wage rates and, until recently, cheaper raw cotton.

[21] Bull. of the Dept. of State, Vol. 53, No. 1354, July 12, 1965, pp. 89-92.

For some years the United States Government operated a two price system for raw cotton under which the American textile manufacturer paid more for cotton produced in this country than foreign competitors paid for the same cotton. For example, American mills were paying about thirty-five cents per pound for cotton grown in the United States when the world price was about eight cents per pound less. At the same time rigid import quotas on raw cotton made American mills captive customers of the cotton growers of this country, preventing them from taking advantage of lower world prices.

The effect of this differential on imports is most obvious in the case of yarn imports where cotton is an important part of total costs. Since 1958, cotton yarn imports rose from 3.9 to over 104.4 million square yards equivalent. Congress finally acted to correct this hardship on the cotton industry by the passage of the Agriculture Act of 1964, which among other things authorized the Secretary of Agriculture through July 31, 1966, to make subsidy payments to domestic cotton handlers or domestic cotton mills on their purchases of United States grown cotton.[22]

The Omnibus Farm Law passed in 1965 extends one price cotton for four years beyond July 31, 1966. Unlike the 1964 act, which offset a market support price by providing an "equalization" payment to domestic users and to exporters which brought their cotton costs down to the world price level, this act provides that the difference between the world price and the desired level of farm income be paid directly to the farmers.[23]

The industry, however, is alarmed about possible changes in the long-term agreement currently being reviewed for renewal. Some countries feel that there is room for greater foreign participation in the American market and therefore urge increases in quotas. Whatever expansion there is in the importation of textiles, the industry hopes that it is not affected adversely; for its continued good health depends on maintaining an orderly production and marketing system.

---

[22] H. R. 6196, Public Law 88-297.
[23] H. R. 9811.

CHAPTER IV

WAGES AND EMPLOYMENT

a. Wages

The textile industry, which made a modest beginning in the latter part of the Eighteenth Century, was not noted for high wages paid employees. Complete records are not available, but sketchy information relating to wages may be found in the books of various companies.

The earliest wages records of Boston Manufacturing Company, founded in 1813, are for May, 1817. With a work week averaging from 78 to 80 hours, the weekly wages for girls working at various jobs were as follows: card room, $2.12 (piece work); spinning room, $2.50; winding room, $3.60 (piece work); weave room, $3.03 (piece work); dressing room, $4.06; bobbin carriers, $2.25. Men employed in the card room were paid $3.67, while department superintendents enjoyed a salary of $10.10 per week. The watchman received $6.40, machinists $7.72, and millwrights $8.87 a week. The highest paid textile workers were mule spinners, two of whom were reported to have received $16.24 and $21.56 a week, but were required to pay for the assistance of their bag boys.[1]

The following table shows the average daily rates of operatives below supervisory grades, for the four departments in the Waltham, Lowell and Slater Mills for the years 1821, 1824 and 1828, respectively.

TABLE II

AVERAGE DAILY RATES OF PAY OF COTTON MILL OPERATIVES
IN CERTAIN NEW ENGLAND MILLS, 1821 TO 1828[2]

Department	Waltham, Mass. Mill, 1821	Lowell, Mass., Mill, 1824	Slater Mill, Rhode Island, 1828
Carding	$ .39	$ .375	$ .31
Spinning	.43	.56	----
Weaving	.45	.67	.50
Dressing	.50	.375	.375

[1] Saco-Lowell Bulletin, 150th Anniversary, pp. 3-4.
[2] "History of Wages in the United States from Colonial Times to 1928," Bur. of Lab. Stat., U.S. Dept. of Labor, No. 499, p. 91.

The working day was long, twelve hours for the Slater Mill, while operatives at Lowell worked from 5 a.m. to 7 p.m. with two half-hour recesses for meals.

The earnings in the weave room at Slater Mills for the month of November, 1828, ranged from $1.25 to $9, while the average monthly wage for the twenty weavers employed (all women) was $7.58. However, during October, 1829, three women earned over $14 on two looms, and in 1830 ten women working on three looms made between $14 and $15 a month.[3]

Second hands in the card room got $1.25 at Lowell and $1 at Providence. At Slater Mill loom fixers received $1.25 a day, the same as overseers, and the superintendent of the Slater's Steam Cotton Manufactory had a fixed salary of $50 a month.[4]

Mule spinners in the Providence Mill were paid $1.33 a day, the highest in the plant except for the carding and weaving overseers. The next year, 1829, piece rates were introduced and mule spinners were paid at the rates of 16 cents per 100 skeins of work, and 13 cents per 100 skeins of filling. Monthly earnings ranged from $36.18 to $44.10 and averaged $39.54. By 1844 the piece rate had dropped to 8½ and 6½ cents per 100 skeins and the highest amount earned in May of that year was $35.70.[5]

Women weavers earned $4.33 a week in 1836 but their wages declined to $2.75 in 1840. With loom improvements, the 1836 level was reached again ten years later and male weavers earned about $1 a week more than women. Inflated prices due to the California gold rush caused operatives earnings in cotton mills to rise about 8 percent between 1850-60.[6]

In 1860 female spinners in Massachusetts averaged 78 hours a week at work and were paid 64 cents a day, while male weavers worked 72 hours a week for 91 cents a day. Female weavers averaged 76 hours a week and their compensation was 66 cents per day.

The following table shows the changes in hours of employment and wages in Massachusetts of spinners and weavers during the last decades of the nineteenth century.[7]

It may be noted that the average number of hours worked by both spinners and weavers in Massachusetts had been reduced to sixty hours per week by 1875. Pay per hour fluctuated during the

---

[3] *Ibid.*, p. 92.
[4] *Ibid.*
[5] *Ibid.*, p. 93.
[6] Victor S. Clark, *History of Manufactures in the United States*, Vol. I, p. 396.
[7] "History of Wages in the United States from Colonial Times to 1928," Bur. of Labor Stat., U.S. Dept. of Labor, No. 499, pp. 386-392.

TABLE III

HOURS AND WAGES OF SPINNERS, WEAVERS OF COTTON GOODS
BY YEAR AND STATE [8]

Year and State	Sex	Spinners Av. Hrs. Per Wk.	Av. Pay Per Day ($)	Sex	Weavers Av. Hrs. Per Wk.	Av. Pay Per Day ($)
Massachusetts						
1865	F	69	.68	F	71	.89
1870	F	66	.93	F	66	1.19
1875	M	60	1.83	F	60	1.16
	F	60	.91	M	†	1.59
1880	M	60	1.66	F	60	1.16
	F	60	.93	M	†	1.31
1885	M	60	1.06	M	60	1.14
	F	60	.91	F	60	.94
1890	M	60	1.61	M	†	1.39
	F	60	.96	F	60	1.16

† Not reported.

period 1865 to 1890 with male employees being paid more than female operatives.

The increase in wages, together with the growth in the number of cotton mill workers in the United States, caused wages paid operatives to more than double in a nineteen year period. In 1870, for example, total wages paid employees in the cotton goods industry amounted to $39,044,000, and by 1899 the amount had increased to $85,126,000.

Toward the end of the past century cotton manufacturing in the Southern states became increasingly important. Rivalry between the North and the South increased, but the South enjoyed an advantage in wages paid operatives, as may be noted in the following table:

TABLE IV

AVERAGE WEEKLY WAGES IN COTTON MILLS, 1890[9]

	Males (in $)	Females (in $)
Massachusetts	$ 8.05	$ 5.89
Maine	7.52	5.68
New Hampshire	7.56	5.83
Connecticut	7.68	5.69
Rhode Island	7.99	5.70
New York	7.62	6.25
Pennsylvania	9.71	6.42
Georgia	5.75	4.55
North Carolina	5.25	3.21
South Carolina	5.17	3.90

[8] A. F. Hinrichs, "Wages in Cotton Goods Manufacturing," Bur. of Lab. Stat., U.S. Dept. of Labor, No. 663, p. 6.
[9] T. M. Young, The American Cotton Industry, p. 134.

It may be noted that while the average weekly pay of operatives in Massachusetts and Pennsylvania was $8.05 and $9.71, it amounted to only $5.75, $5.25 and $5.17 in Georgia, North Carolina and South Carolina, respectively.

Differences in hours of work per week and pay per hour for male weavers in various states is noted in the following table.

TABLE V

WAGES AND HOURS OF WEAVERS, MALES, COTTON GOODS, BY STATE AND YEAR[10]

	Massachusetts		Rhode Island		North Carolina		South Carolina	
Year	Hrs. Per Week	Rate Per Hr.	Hrs. Per Week	Rate Per Hr.	Hrs. Per Week	Rate Per Hr.	Hrs. Per Week	Rate Per Hr.
1907	58	$ .179	50	$ .192	66.0	$ .124	61.5	$ .132
1910	56	.163	56	.179	62.7	.132	60.0	.136
1914	54	.186	54	.201	60.0	.156	60.0	.148
1920	48	.598	49.4	.607	55.1	.582	55.0	.532
1924	48	.543	52.6	.542	55.3	.401	55.0	.328
1926	49	.459	50.1	.494	55.6	.353	55.0	.314
1928	50	.431	52.2	.498	55.9	.370	55.0	.313

The hours of work per week for weavers, as shown in the above table, is typical of cotton mill workers. During the period 1907 to 1928 there was both a reduction of hours and an increase in the hourly pay for operatives in the four states mentioned above. However, throughout the period the working hours were longer and the hourly pay lower in North and South Carolina than in Massachusetts and Rhode Island.

In 1930 the average full time hour per week for male operatives in North and South Carolina were 55.8 and 55, while it was 49 and 51.8 in Massachusetts and Rhode Island. The average hourly earnings in 1930 in North and South Carolina was $.322 and $.292 and in Massachusetts and Rhode Island it amounted to $.431 and $.440.[11]

The average pay per hour for males in twelve cotton manufacturing states in 1930 ranged from 27.9 cents to 49.2 cents; for females from 21.7 to 40 cents; and for both sexes combined for the industry ranged from 25.5 to 45 cents.[12]

During the depression Northern wages were decreased more than Southern wages and in 1932 hourly earnings in the North were 32.3 cents as compared with 23.9 cents in the South. In July, 1933, Southern wages were about 25 percent less than Northern wages or about

[10] Bur. of Lab. Stat., No. 499, p. 394.
[11] Bur. of Lab. Stat. No. 539, p. 9.
[12] Ibid., p. 8.

7 cents an hour. Minimum wages established under the N.R.A. Code in 1934 reduced the difference in wages to 6.6 cents with the Southern earnings about 15 percent less than Northern wages.[13]

Increases in wages in textiles were more general in Northern than in Southern mills in 1936 and 1937. By July, 1937, Northern mills averaged 50 cents and Southern mills 39.7 cents, a difference of 10.3 cents, with Southern wages slightly more than 20 percent under those of the Northern states. Reductions in wages in mills in both areas, but more generally in the North, reduced the difference to 8 cents in August, 1938, with Southern wages 18 percent under those of the North.[14]

In August 1938 the average hourly earnings of cotton mill workers in the United States was 38.3 cents, the average in Northern mills was 44.6 and in Southern mills, 36.5 cents. But Northern cotton mills, generally speaking, paid less than was paid for similar types of skill in other Northern industries. However, in the South cotton textile wages were not notably lower than wages in other industries and were considered higher than wages paid for agricultural work.[15]

In noting the wage differential between Northern and Southern mills, A. F. Hinrichs, chief economist of the Bureau for Labor Statistics, concluded:

> Despite the fact that Southern high-wage mills build up at an average of 40 to 42.5 cents, while the characteristic Northern concentration is at 42.5 to 45 cents, Southern high wage mills pay the same wages to semiskilled workers as do Northern mills. There is a fairly persistent tendency for higher wages to be paid semiskilled workers in Southern mills and for lower wages to be paid to the unskilled, than are paid in the Northern mills with corresponding average earnings for the mill as a whole. This means in effect that Southern mills averaging 40 to 42.5 cents are paying semiskilled workers about the same rate as is paid semiskilled workers in Northern mills averaging 42.5 to 45 cents.[16]

Many Southern cotton mills offered additional benefits to operatives such as low rental homes, recreational facilities and free water and electricity, or at wholesale rates. These cannot easily be reduced to a dollar and cents basis, but the savings realized by them for cotton mill workers diminished the North-South wage differential.

---

[13] H. F. Hinrichs, "Wages in Cotton-Goods Manufacturing," Bur. of Lab. Stat., Bull. No. 663, p. 71.

[14] *Ibid.*, pp. 71-72.

[15] *Ibid.*, p. 144.

[16] *Ibid.*, p. 76. This statement made in 1938 does not seem to be in agreement with the report made in 1940. See Table 6.

Hourly earnings in the industry in September, 1940, averaged 40.3 cents. Of all cotton mill workers, 22.9 percent earned 32.5 cents the minimum wages in 1940. Another 29.6 percent earned between 32.5 and 37.5 cents, 14 per cent 50 cents or more an hour while 3.2 per cent earned 62.5 cents or more.

Summary figures by region, skill and sex are included in Table VI.

TABLE VI

AVERAGE HOURLY EARNINGS OF COTTON-GOODS WORKERS, SEPTEMBER, 1940
BY REGION, SKILL AND SEX[17]

| | All Workers | | | Skilled Workers | | | Semiskilled Workers | | |
Region	Total	Male	Female	Total	Male	Female	Total	Male	Female
U. S.	$0.403	$0.417	$0.377	$0.504	$0.514	$0.450	$0.380	$0.387	$0.372
North	.469	.501	.423	.591	.614	.502	.438	.464	.420
South	.385	.396	.362	.474	.482	.425	.366	.373	.357

UNSKILLED WORKERS

Region	Total	Total	Female
United States	$0.345	$0.345	$0.345
North	.380	.386	.367
South	.334	.334	.335

Earnings in the North averaged .469 as compared with .385 an hour in the South and were also higher in the various skill and sex groups than in the South.

The trend closing the gap between the earnings of cotton mill workers in the North and South began in 1900. At the beginning of World War II the average hourly earnings in Southern cotton mills were about 18 percent less than the average hourly earnings in Northern mills. By 1945 the percentage had been reduced from 18 to 14 percent and during the past decade the difference has been less significant. In 1960, for example, the average hourly earnings for all production workers in textiles in New England was $1.57 as compared with $1.45 in the Southern states.

A comparison of average hours and earnings of production workers in selected manufacturing industries for 1945 through 1949 may be noted in Table VII.

As shown in Table VII, the hourly earnings of production workers in textile mill products increased from 75.7 cents in 1945 to 118.9 cents in January, 1949. During this five year period the hourly earnings of textile operatives advanced from the lowest to the highest of the four industries.

---

[17] *Monthly Labor Review,* Vol. 53, p. 1500.

TABLE VII[18]

AVERAGE HOURS AND EARNINGS OF PRODUCTION WORKERS IN FURNITURE AND
FINISHED LUMBER PRODUCTS, TEXTILE MILL PRODUCTS, APPAREL AND
FINISHED TEXTILE PRODUCTS AND TOBACCO MANUFACTURES, 1945-1949

	Furniture and Finished Lumber Products			Textile Mills Products		
	Hourly Earnings	Weekly Hours	Weekly Earnings	Hourly Earnings	Weekly Hours	Weekly Earnings
Year	in ¢'s		in $'s	in ¢'s		in $'s
1945	84.8	43.3	36.68	75.7	41.1	31.08
1946	93.6	41.9	39.22	89.3	40.2	35.89
1947	106.3	41.7	44.36	103.5	39.5	40.94
1948	115.3	41.1	47.38	115.8	39.1	45.27
1949 (Jan. only)	118.3	39.8	47.08	118.9	37.4	44.47

	Apparel and Finished Textile Products			Tobacco Manufactures		
	Hourly Earnings	Weekly Hours	Weekly Earnings	Hourly Earnings	Weekly Hours	Weekly Earnings
Year	in ¢'s		in $'s	in ¢'s		in $'s
1945	85.8	36.9	31.67	46.4	41.7	31.79
1946	46.7	36.9	35.62	86.8	39.5	34.25
1947	102.8	36.3	37.28	95.1	38.6	36.67
1948	108.4	36.0	39.02	99.5	38.0	37.78
1949 (Jan. only)	112.3	35.2	39.63	102.0	36.4	37.13

During the period from 1953 through 1964 the earnings of employees in the textile mill products industry steadily increased. This advance is shown in Table VIII as well as the average earnings in all manufacturing industries and the apparel industry.

It may be noted that the average hourly earnings of textile mill products workers increased from $1.36 in 1953 to $1.78 in 1964, while their average weekly earnings advanced from $53.18 to $72.98 during the same period. In 1953 the average hourly and weekly earnings for workers in all manufacturing industries was $1.74 and $70.47, and for employees of the apparel industries they amounted to $1.35 and $48.74. By 1964 average hourly earnings for all manufacturing industries had increased to $2.53, and weekly to $102.97. During the same period average earnings for apparel and related industries workers advanced to $1.79 per hour and $64.26 per week.

The average hourly and weekly earnings of textile mill products employees in November, 1965, were $1.91 and $80.79 respectively, as compared with $1.85 hourly and $67.34 weekly for apparel and related products workers. For all manufacturing industries the aver-

---

[18] *The Economic Almanac 1950*, National Conference Board, pp. 354-355.

38

TABLE VIII

AVERAGE WEEKLY HOURS AND AVERAGE WEEKLY AND HOURLY EARNINGS IN
ALL MANUFACTURING INDUSTRIES, TEXTILE MILL PRODUCTS INDUSTRY
AND THE APPAREL INDUSTRY, 1953-1964[19]

	Average Weekly Hours			Average Weekly Earnings		
Year	All Manu-facturing Industries	Textile Mill Products	Apparel Industry	All Manu-facturing Industries	Textile Mill Products	Apparel Industry
1953	40.5	39.1	36.1	$ 76.47	$ 53.18	$ 48.74
1954	39.6	38.3	35.3	70.49	52.09	48.36
1955	40.7	40.1	36.3	75.70	55.34	49.73
1956	40.4	39.7	36.0	98.78	57.17	52.92
1957	39.8	38.9	35.7	81.59	57.96	53.91
1958	39.2	38.6	35.1	82.71	57.51	54.05
1959	40.3	40.4	36.3	88.26	63.02	56.63
1960	39.7	39.5	35.44	89.72	63.60	56.29
1961	39.8	39.9	35.4	92.34	65.04	58.06
1962	40.4	40.6	36.2	96.56	68.21	61.18
1963	40.5	40.6	36.1	99.63	69.43	62.45
1964	40.7	41.0	35.9	102.97	72.98	64.26

AVERAGE HOURLY EARNINGS

	All Manu-facturing Industries	Textile Mill Products	Apparel Industry
1953	$1.74	$1.36	$1.35
1954	1.78	1.36	1.37
1955	1.86	1.38	1.37
1956	1.95	1.44	1.47
1957	2.05	1.49	1.51
1958	2.11	1.49	1.54
1959	2.19	1.56	1.56
1960	2.26	1.61	1.59
1961	2.32	1.63	1.64
1962	2.39	1.68	1.69
1963	2.46	1.71	1.73
1964	2.53	1.78	1.79

age hourly earnings were $2.64 and weekly $109.30 during the same period.[20]

A survey completed in 1963 by the Bureau of Labor Statistics showed men operatives averaged $1.56 an hour compared to $1.47 for women. In the Southeast the wage advantage for men was 10 cents and in New England 14 cents an hour. Contributing to this

---

[19] Bur. of Lab. Stat., U. S. Department of Labor.
[20] *Employment and Earnings,* Vol. 12, No. 6, Bur. of Lab. Stat., Dec. 1965.

difference was the holding of jobs with different pay levels—that is, more women were employed in positions requiring less skill than the work commonly done by men.

Earnings of men and women in the same job were often about the same. For example, male time-rated warper tenders averaged $1.44, compared to $1.45 for female tenders in the Southeast. Also, men and women loom weavers in the Southeast averaged the same pay, $1.72 an hour.

This 1963 survey, in referring to the practices of the cotton textile industry, noted that almost all cotton mills had three-shift operations. While the second-shift workers rarely received differential pay, third-shift employees (one-fifth of workers in New England and one-fourth in the Southeast) in New England received 7 cents an hour above day rates compared with 5 cents in the Southeast.

Also reported was that paid holidays were given annually to three-fourths of the production workers. Practically all operatives in New England received six days while a fourth of the workers in the Southeastern mills received paid holidays, usually one day a year. Paid vacations, after qualifying periods of service, were enjoyed by practically all workers in the textile industry. Typical provisions for operatives were one week's pay after one year of service and two weeks after five years or more.

The 1963 survey by the Bureau of Labor Statistics also reported that life, hospital and surgical insurance, financed at least in part by the employer, was carried by mills employing more than nine-tenths of the workers. About half the operatives were employed in mills providing accidental death and dismemberment insurance and sickness and accident insurance. Medical insurance was available to about one-third of the workers.

According to the 1963 survey, pension plans providing regular payments for the remainder of an operative's life upon retirement (in addition to federal old-age insurance) were in force in mills employing about one-fourth of the production workers. These plans applied to 29 per cent of the operatives in the Southeast and to 3 per cent in New England. Plans providing lump sum payments at retirement (not common in the Southeast) applies to 92 per cent of the workers in New England. Likewise, profit sharing on bonuses at Christmas or at other times were provided at mills employing about a fifth of the production and office workers. In New England bonuses were available to about one-tenth, and in the Southeast to about one-fifth of the production workers.[21]

---

[21] *Ibid.*, pp. 6-7.

b. Employment

During the early part of the nineteenth century cotton mills began to replace the homespun industry in the United States. By 1831 the number of mills had increased to 801 and the number of workers exceeded 62,000. The growth in the number of establishments and wage earners is shown in Table 9, by years.

TABLE IX

NUMBER OF MILLS, WAGE EARNERS IN COTTON GOODS INDUSTRY IN THE UNITED STATES—1831-1960

Year	Mills	Wage Earners (Avg. for yr.)
1831	801	62,208
1840	1240	72,119
1850	1094	92,286
1860	1091	122,028
1870	956	135,369
1880	756	172,544
1889	905	218,876
1904	1077	310,458
1909	1208	371,182
1914	1179	379,361
1919	1288	430,966
1921	1328	412,058
1923	1375	471,503
1925	1366	445,184
1929	1347	467,596
1931	1140	329,962
1933	1057	379,445
1935	1042	369,062
1937	----	432,885
1940	----	411,800
1942	----	505,900
1945	----	414,700
1946 (April-May)	----	494,810
1952 (March)	----	390,897
1954 (November)	----	352,953
1960 (August)	----	277,138

Source: U. S. Dept. of Labor, Bulletin No. 663, p. 6; *Statistical Abstracts of the United States*, 1935-1961.

During the decade 1850 to 1860 the wage earners in cotton mills exceeded 100,000 and had passed 200,000 by 1889. In 1904 the operatives numbered 310,000 and in 1923 reached 471,503, which was the peak of employment in the industry until 1942 when a monthly average of 505,900 wage earners were employed.

41

The August 1960 total number of wage earners was approximately 20 per cent lower than that recorded in November 1954, and almost 30 per cent below the level of March 1952. This decline in employment has not affected adversely production for, according to information published by the Bureau of the Census, the production of cotton broadwoven goods in 1960 was only slightly lower than in 1954 and about the same as in 1952. This was possible because during recent years technological changes have increased the industry's output per worker.

More recently, cotton mill workers have been grouped with other textile workers and under the general designation "Textile Mill Products Industry."[22] Accordingly, Table X gives the total number of employees in Textile Mill Products Industry as well as for all manufacturing industries and Apparel and Related Products Industry.

TABLE X[23]

TOTAL NUMBER OF EMPLOYEES IN ALL MANUFACTURING, TEXTILE MILL PRODUCTS AND APPAREL AND RELATED PRODUCTS INDUSTRIES
1950-1965
(in thousands of employees)

Year	All Manufacturing Industries	Textile Mill Products Industry	Apparel and Related Products Industry
		Monthly Averages for Each Year	
1950	15,241	1,256	1,202
1951	16,393	1,238	1,207
1952	16,632	1,162	1,216
1953	17,549	1,155	1,248
1954	16,314	1,042	1,184
1955	16,882	1,050	1,219
1956	17,243	1,032	1,223
1957	17,174	981	1,210
1958	15,945	919	1,172
1959	16,675	946	1,226
1960	16,796	924	1,233
1961	16,327	893	1,214
1962	16,853	902	1,263
1963	17,005	889	1,284
1964	17,303	899	1,310
1965 (June)	18,045	923	1,382

It may be noted that during the 1950-1964 period the total number of employees in all manufacturing industries increased from

[22] Bur. of Lab. Stat. Bull. No. 663, p. 6, Bur. of the Census.
[23] Source: U. S. Dept. of Labor.

15,241,000 to 18,045,000, while employees in apparel and related products increased from 1,202,000 to 1,382,000. During the same period, however, the number of employees in the textile mill products industry decreased from 1,256,000 to 923,000. It would appear, however, that the textile mill products industry employs one person out of every twenty engaged in manufacturing, a position which the cotton goods industry enjoyed for about a century.

Textile mill executives fully expect the trend toward mechanization and automation to continue. The introduction of the more sophisticated equipment and processes will require changes in the skill of employees. A quarter of a century ago it was estimated that about 56 per cent of all cotton mill workers were semi-skilled, 23 per cent skilled, and over 20 per cent unskilled.[24] Requirements in the industry today demand upgrading of operatives. To meet this demand, on-the-job-training programs have been instituted and old employees have thus acquired new skills. New employees are coming to the mills with better formal education, and more often with better technical training than those of twenty-five years ago. They, too, will doubtless want to progress with the industry by participating in training programs.

[24] Bur. of Labor Stat. Serial No. L. 1414, p. 4.

CHAPTER V

MAN-MADE FIBERS

While Robert Hooke, an English scientist, in 1664 suggested the possibility of mechanically duplicating the work of the silk worm and, in 1710, René A. F. Réaumur, a French physicist, contended the fibers might be formed from gums or resins since silk itself was but a dried gum, it was more than a century later before material results were realized. Projecting by the experiments and findings of various predecessors, Count Hilaire de Chardonnet in 1884 took out the first patent on a nitro-cellular fiber.[1]

Chardonnet had studied the habits, processes and anatomy of the silk worms, and for thirty years he experimented with the hope of developing a product like that which developed from a diet of Mulberry leaves exclusively. His product, commonly known as "Chardonnet silk," was exhibited at the Paris Exposition in 1889 and attracted much attention. Funds were forthcoming and the first artificial silk factory was established at Besançon.[2] However the fabric of nitro-cellulose was highly inflammable and caused so many fires that the government ordered the factory closed. Later an English scientist, Sir Joseph Sevan, devised a demitrating process which removed the explosive character so the Besançon factory reopened and enjoyed successful operation.[3]

This Nitro-Cellulose process, the only one known for some years, was not entirely satisfactory and finally led to the establishment of the Cupro-Ammonium process patented by Depaissis in 1900.

Other important developments followed with the patenting of Viscose in 1892 and acetate in 1895 by C. F. Cross and E. J. Bevan, English chemists. The acetate patentees had the benefit of early discoveries in this area made by Schutzenbugen in 1865 and Franchimont in 1879.[4]

The first viscose yarn was exhibited in Paris in 1900 and with the invention of the centrifugal spinning box by D. F. Topham the manufacture of artificial silk was really launched.[5]

---

[1] H. R. Mauersberger and E. W. K. Schwarz, *Rayon and Staple Fiber Handbook,* pp. 1-2.
[2] Mois H. Avram, *The Rayon Industry,* pp. 5-6.
[3] H. F. Woods and F. E. Ackerman, *The Rayon Industry in the United States,* pp. 4-5.
[4] *Ibid.,* p. 6.
[5] H. R. Mauersberger and E. W. K. Schwarz, *Rayon and Staple Fiber Handbook,* p. 5.

The cellulose acetate process was discovered earlier and extensively studied. It did not receive any technical value however until 1901 when Cross and Bevan directed attention to its potentialities.[6] While its popularity has grown during the past decades, it has not gained as great a public acceptance as has the viscose process.

In spite of various efforts in Europe, only two successful artificial silk plants were in operation prior to 1911. Two attempts to manufacture it in America ended in bankruptcies. However, in 1910, the first successful commercial viscose plant was established at Marcus Hook, Pennsylvania. This establishment, the American Viscose Company, was almost wholly owned by the English textile house of Courtauld, Ltd.[7]

For some years, artificial silk did not gain great favor with American consumers. It did not feel, look, wash, or wear like silk; but it was cheaper and so, satisfied the demand for cheap hosiery and underwear.

Various silk manufacturers and a portion of the American public objected to the use of the name "artificial silk." Confusion existed in the retail and consumer circles so various new names such as "Glos," "Chardonnet," and "Filatex" were suggested. Finally the National Dry Goods Association set up a committee, about 1924, to select an appropriate name, and the term "Rayon" was adopted.[8]

The American Viscose Company, largely because of the industrial experience of its parent company, enjoyed success in the production of rayon. For over a decade it made the only domestic rayon sold in commercially important quantities on the American market, furnishing approximately seventy-five per cent of the rayon consumed in the United States.[9]

During the early 1920's, six new companies began producing rayon, four of which received assistance in one form or another from European companies. Two had the cooperation of the French and Italian viscose syndicates, a third had obtained licenses from a Belgium concern, and a fourth was organized by a British company which was the first to develop the cellulose acetate process in England.[10]

Also during this decade several depressed cotton mills began experimenting with weaving, dyeing and finishing of rayon, and by

    [6] The Viscose Company, *The Story of Rayon*, p. 12.
    [7] H. F. Woods and F. E. Ackerman, *The Rayon Industry in the United States*, p. 6.
    [8] Robert B. Evans, *A Survey of Development and Use of Rayon and Other Synthetic Fibers*, p. 4.
    [9] The Viscose Company, *The Story of Rayon*, p. 16.
    [10] U. S. Tariff Comm., *The Rayon Industry*, p. 72.

1927 the cotton textile industry had developed a section that was weaving rayon on cotton machinery and selling the product according to the cotton method of distribution.[11] During the course of a few years, the manufacturers recognized the adaptations to be made in cotton textile machinery, and, working in conjunction with textile machinery manufacturers, they constructed special rayon equipment. Thus rayon manufacturers made progress in quantity output, and, through advancement in chemical and engineering technique, production costs were lowered making available better quality yarn at a lower price.

During the depression period beginning in 1929, there was little expansion in the physical aspects of the industry but commencing in 1934 additional units were constructed and those already in production were enlarged.[12]

In 1928, Charles M. A. Sine, Vice President of E. I. du Pont de Nemours and Company, started a research program which under the direction of Walter H. Carothers led to the manufacture of nylon. The cellulosic fibers, previously described, were made from fiber formed in nature, but nylon was produced by chemical synthesis.[13] The success of the research was recognized by 1935, and in 1938, a $8,600,000 plant was started in Seaford, Delaware. Months before it was in full production, du Pont authorized an additional $6,400,000 for an addition to double capacity. In December, 1939, after eleven years of research and development, the first nylon continuous filament yarn was produced in a commercial plant. The original capacity of the plant was estimated at four million pounds a year—about enough to make 10 or 15 per cent of the 43 million dozen pairs of full-fashion silk hose then sold in the United States each year. This plant also had the nylon capacity to throw about 7,500,000,000 Japanese silk worms into technological unemployment in addition to reducing the work of some 418,000 Japanese farmers, silk workers, cocoon brokers and inspectors then involved in getting an equivalent amount of raw silk to the United States.[14]

Nylon's first use was for women's hosiery in which it made an immediate appeal. A rush to hosiery counters on May 15, 1940 swept the first day quota of five million pairs of nylon hose almost out of stock.[15] The rapidity with which nylon replaced silk and rayon may be noted in the following table.

[11] U. S. Dept. of Com., *Wool and Manmade Fibers in the U.S.*, p. 2.
[12] U. S. Tariff Com., *The Rayon Industry*, p. 73.
[13] See R. W. Monocrieff, *Man-Made Fibers*, pp. 299-355.
[14] "Nylon," *Fortune Magazine*, Vol. XXII, July 1940, p. 114.
[15] *Ibid.*, p. 57.

TABLE XI

WOMEN'S FULL-FASHIONED AND SEAMLESS NYLON, RAYON AND SILK HOSIERY:
PERCENTAGE OF U. S. POPULATION BY TYPE OF FIBER, 1930-1954[16]

Year	Nylon	Rayon	Silk	Total
1939		7.5	92.5	100.0
1940	5.8	9.2	85.0	100.0
1941	18.1	14.6	67.3	100.0
1946	62.9	32.8	4.3	100.0
1947	82.2	15.4	2.4	100.0
1948	93.4	5.6	1.0	100.0
1949	96.0	3.4	0.6	100.0
1950	97.5	2.1	0.4	100.0
1951	97.5	2.1	0.4	100.0
1952	98.1	1.7	0.2	100.0
1953	98.5	1.3	0.2	100.0
1954	98.7	1.1	0.2	100.0

The years 1942 through 1945 were omitted from the above table because during that period the entire output of nylon was allocated for war uses. It made America independent of silk and proved to be superior material to silk for parachutes. Nylon also was found to be more resistant to the effects of salt water, far less affected by mildew and damaging insects than most other fabrics including silk. Nylon cord bomber tires were used as early as 1941 and performed well during World War II. Nylon towing rope was developed for gliders, and nylon paint brushes replaced those made of long bristles from hogs in China and Siberia which could not be obtained from those areas during the war period.[17]

While nylon has enjoyed a great triumph in hosiery since World War II, it suffered a defeat in shirts. It gained in fashion wear, floor coverings, sweaters, dresses and children's wear, and it blends well with cotton and rayon for men's work garments and boys' wear.[18]

After some years of research acrylic fibers were introduced to the American market by E. I. du Pont de Nemours and Company in 1950. This new product, known as Orlon, was produced in Camden, South Carolina, and was followed by American Cyanamid's Creslan, Chemstrand's Acrilan and Dow Chemical's Zefkrome and Zefran. In 1949 Union Carbide and Carbon Corporation developed a modified acrylic fiber, Dynel, produced at Charleston, West Virginia.

[16] Source: National Association of Hosiery Manufacturers.
[17] G. P. Hoff, "New Developments and Uses of Nylon," *Rayon Textile Monthly*, Vol. 24, August, 1943, pp. 409-411.
[18] "New Trends in Nylon," *Modern Textile Magazine*, Vol. 38, Sept. 1957, pp. 56-58.

Another modacrylic, Verel, was developed by Eastman Kodak Company.

Acrylic fibers are produced from acrylonitride which is composed of elements taken from coal, air, water, petroleum and limestone. These fibers are used in apparel for men and women, draperies and carpets.

The polyester fibers were experimented with during the 1930's but the first successful one of this class, trade-name Terylene, was discovered by J. W. Whinfield and J. T. Dickson in England.[19] The right to produce this commodity was acquired by Du Pont in 1946 and a plant was erected in Kinston, North Carolina to manufacture the fiber which was later marketed under the name of Dacron. More recently other firms have begun production of this fiber, for example, Tennessee Eastman's Kodel and Fiber Industries, Fortrel. The material is used for women's blouses, and dresses, men's shirts and upholstery.

Other synthetic fibers in production in the United States are Spandex, Olefin, Saran, Nytril, Vinyon and Vinal, meeting various demands of consumers in this country.[20]

The physical and chemical characteristics of most of the newer fibers are described generally speaking as: 1. High in tension strength relative to weight. 2. Resistant to abrasion. 3. Dimensionally stable. 4. Low in moisture absorption and retention. 5. Resistant to bacteriological damage. 6. Free from attack by insects or vermin. 7. Affected only slightly or not at all by most common acids and alkalis. 8. Not flammable. 9. Heat resistant up to the melting point, which varies. 10. Washable. 11. High in electric insulation properties. 12. Subject to developing static electricity easily. 13. Difficult to dye except by use of special dyeing techniques. 14. Subject to pilling in certain cases. 15. Relatively low in melting points, which in certain cases, amounts to heat sensitivity.[21]

In manufacturing fibers, it is possible to fit them to specific needs. Their fineness and luster can be changed and their colors, once established, do not rub or wash off and show exceptional resistance to fading. These and other fine qualities of man-made fibers, having been recognized by the American people, gave impetus to the tremendous expansion of the industry in this country. This industry produced about a million pounds of fiber in 1912 and the amount

19 J. R. Whinefield, "The Development of Terylene," *Textile Research Journal,* Vol. 23, May 1953, pp. 289-294.
20 For a description of the structure and properties of fibers see R. D. Moncrieff, *Man-Made Fibers.*
21 "Wool and Man-Made Fibers in the United States," U. S. Dept. of Com. (1956), p. 5.

produced increased to 475.8 million in 1940, 1,405.3 in 1950, 1,882.7 in 1960, and to 2,691 million pounds in 1963.[22] This industry's growth has to a large extent been due to its close integration with the chemical industry and to the techniques and resources which the industry made available.

For many years cotton and wool have occupied a predominant position in the fiber field. The table which follows shows the decline of the natural fibers and the growth of man-made fibers in mill consumption in this country.

TABLE XII

TOTAL MILL CONSUMPTION COTTON, WOOL AND MAN-MADE FIBERS,
UNITED STATES 1920 TO 1960[23]

U. S. MILL CONSUMPTION OF 4 FIBERS INCLUDING MAN-MADE FIBERS

Year	Cotton Lb.	%	Wool Lb.	%	Silk Lb.	%	Total Man-Made Lb.	%	Total Lb.	%
1920	2,822.8	88.6	314.2	9.9	38.8	1.2	8.7	0.3	3,184.5	100
1921	2,600.6	86.2	343.4	11.4	51.8	1.7	19.8	0.7	3,015.6	100
1922	2,911.3	85.6	406.5	12.0	57.8	1.7	24.9	0.7	3,400.5	100
1923	3,122.6	85.8	422.4	11.6	61.5	1.7	32.3	0.9	3,638.8	100
1924	2,636.5	85.6	342.2	11.1	59.6	1.9	42.3	1.4	3,080.6	100
1925	3,075.3	86.4	349.9	9.8	76.0	2.2	58.2	1.6	3,559.4	100
1926	3,213.5	87.0	342.7	9.3	76.9	2.1	60.6	1.6	3,693.7	100
1927	3,590.1	86.9	354.1	8.6	85.0	2.1	99.6	2.4	4,128.8	100
1928	3,187.0	86.0	333.2	9.0	87.2	2.3	100.2	2.7	3,707.6	100
1929	3,425.3	85.1	368.1	9.2	96.8	2.4	133.2	3.3	4,023.4	100
1930	2,616.6	85.0	263.2	8.5	80.6	2.6	119.3	3.9	3,079.7	100
1931	2,654.9	82.6	311.0	9.7	87.5	2.7	159.3	5.0	3,212.7	100
1932	2,463.7	84.2	230.1	7.9	74.8	2.6	155.4	5.3	2,924.0	100
1933	3,050.7	83.5	317.1	8.7	70.4	1.9	217.3	5.9	3,655.5	100
1934	2,659.5	84.2	229.7	7.3	60.4	1.9	207.0	6.6	3,156.6	100
1935	2,755.4	78.3	417.5	11.9	72.4	2.0	273.7	7.8	3,519.0	100
1936	3,471.4	80.9	406.1	9.5	67.5	1.6	343.2	8.0	4,288.2	100
1937	3,646.6	82.5	380.8	8.6	64.2	1.4	329.5	7.5	4,421.1	100
1938	2,918.3	81.1	284.5	7.9	57.1	1.6	340.1	9.4	3,600.0	100
1939	3,628.6	79.7	396.5	8.7	55.3	1.2	473.0	10.4	4,553.4	100
1940	3,959.1	80.6	407.9	8.3	47.6	1.0	498.7	10.1	4,913.3	100
1941	5,192.1	80.1	648.0	10.0	25.6	0.4	617.5	9.5	6,483.2	100
1942	5,633.1	81.7	603.6	8.7	0.2		658.9	9.6	6,895.8	100
1943	5,270.6	79.6	636.2	9.6	----	----	712.8	10.8	6,619.6	100
1944	4,790.4	77.4	622.8	10.1	----	----	772.5	12.5	6,185.7	100
1945	4,515.8	75.2	645.1	10.7	1.0		845.1	14.1	6,007.0	100
1946	4,809.1	73.8	737.5	11.3	13.5	0.2	954.3	14.7	6,514.4	100
1947	4,665.6	72.6	698.2	10.9	3.2		1,057.9	16.5	6,424.9	100
1948	4,463.5	69.7	693.1	10.8	7.4	0.1	1,239.7	19.4	6,403.7	100
1949	3,839.1	70.5	500.4	9.2	4.0	0.1	1,101.9	20.2	5,445.4	100
1950	4,682.7	68.4	634.8	9.3	10.5	0.1	1,518.4	22.2	6,846.4	100
1951	4,868.6	71.2	484.1	7.1	7.2	0.1	1,478.6	21.6	6,838.5	100
1952	4,470.9	69.4	466.4	7.3	12.6	0.2	1,490.2	23.1	6,440.1	100
1953	4,456.1	68.8	493.9	7.6	7.8	0.1	1,523.7	23.5	6,481.5	100
1954	4,127.3	68.5	384.1	6.4	8.5	0.1	1,508.3	25.0	6,028.2	100
1955	4,382.4	65.3	413.8	6.2	11.0	0.2	1,902.5	28.3	6,709.7	100
1956	4,362.6	66.7	440.8	6.7	12.7	0.2	1,727.4	26.4	6,543.5	100
1957	4,060.4	65.2	368.8	5.9	8.3	0.1	1,792.6	28.8	6,230.1	100
1958	3,867.0	64.8	331.1	5.5	5.3	0.1	1,764.1	29.6	5,967.5	100
1959	4,337.1	63.4	429.2	6.3	8.0	0.1	2,064.8	30.2	6,839.1	100
1960	4,203.2	64.8	404.2	6.2	6.9	0.1	1,877.6	28.9	6,491.9	100

[22] *Textile Organon*, Vol. 35, No. 2, p. 20.
[23] U. S. Dept. of Agri., *Basic Book of Textile Statistics, Textile Organon*, Vol. 33, No. 1 (1962).

It may be noted in the above table that of the total mill consumption of fibers that the percentage of cotton consumed declined from 88.6 per cent in 1920 to 64.8 per cent in 1960. In 1938 the total weight of man-made fibers first exceeded the total wool consumption and except in 1941 stayed ahead. Since 1950 wool has taken a drop in percentage of total fiber consumption and in 1960 about four and one-half times more man-made fibers than wool was consumed in American mills.

Per Capita Consumption of Fibers

On a per capita basis, consumption of fibers at mills trended upward during the pre-World-War-II period as consumption increased at a faster rate than population. In the postwar period mill fiber consumption increased at a slower rate than population, reflecting a downward trend in per capita fiber construction as may be noted in the following table.

TABLE XIII

COTTON, WOOL, MAN-MADE FIBERS: CONSUMPTION, PER CAPITA; MILL, ACTUAL DOMESTIC AND COTTON EQUIVALENT DOMESTIC, 1920 TO 1960

Year	Cotton Lb.	Wool Lb.	Man-made fibers Lb.	Total Lb.	Year	Cotton Lb.	Wool Lb.	Man-made fibers Lb.	Total Lb.
1920	26.5	3.0	0.1	29.5	1940	30.0	3.1	3.8	36.8
1921	24.0	3.2	.2	27.3	1941	38.9	4.9	4.6	48.4
1922	26.4	3.7	.2	30.4	1942	41.8	4.5	4.9	51.1
1923	27.9	3.8	.3	31.9	1943	38.6	4.7	5.2	48.4
1924	23.1	3.0	.4	26.5	1944	34.6	4.5	5.6	44.7
1925	26.7	3.0	.5	30.1	1945	32.3	4.6	6.0	42.9
1926	27.4	2.9	.5	30.8	1946	34.0	5.2	6.8	46.0
1927	30.2	3.0	.8	34.0	1947	32.4	4.8	7.3	44.6
1928	26.4	2.7	.8	30.0	1948	30.4	4.7	8.5	43.6
1929	28.1	3.0	1.1	32.2	1949	25.7	3.4	7.9	36.5
1930	21.3	2.1	1.0	24.4	1950	30.9	4.2	10.0	45.1
1931	21.4	2.5	1.3	25.2	1951	31.5	3.1	9.6	44.2
1932	19.7	1.8	1.3	22.8	1952	28.5	3.0	9.5	40.9
1933	24.3	2.5	1.7	28.5	1953	27.9	3.1	9.6	40.6
1934	21.0	1.8	1.6	24.5	1954	25.4	2.4	9.3	37.1
1935	21.7	3.3	2.2	27.1	1955	26.5	2.5	11.5	40.5
1936	27.1	3.2	2.7	33.0	1956	25.9	2.6	10.3	38.8
1937	28.3	3.0	2.6	33.8	1957	23.7	2.2	10.5	36.3
1938	22.5	2.2	2.6	27.3	1958	22.2	1.9	10.1	34.2
1939	27.7	3.0	3.6	34.4	1959	24.5	2.4	11.7	38.6
					1960	23.2	2.3	10.4	35.8

Source: U. S. Dept. of Agriculture Tech. Bull. No. 1301 (1963).

It may be observed that the per capita consumption of all fibers increased by 6.3 pounds from 1920 to 1960. For the same period, per capita consumption of man-made fibers increased by 10.3 pounds, while wool and cotton decreased by .7 and 3.3 pounds respectively, per capita.

The total mill and the per capita consumption of fibers having been ascertained, the end use of the fibers may be examined. Data published by the Textile Economics Bureau designates the following end uses: 1. men and boys' wear, (2) women's and misses' wear, (3) children's and infants' wear, (4) home furnishings, (5) other consumer type products, (6) industrial uses and (7) exports and domestic products.

There are, however, some limitations which should be noted when considering this data. There is the question of the reliability of the data supplied by the United States Census Bureau. Many of the apparel item poundages are based on cuttings data supplied by the Bureau whose reports frequently break down the total number of garments cut into two or more fibers—for example, cotton (or chiefly cotton) and wool (100% wool or chiefly wool or 50% or more wool). The great increase in the use of fabrics containing blends and mixtures of man-made fibers, cotton and/or wool makes accurate reporting almost impossible.

An exact balance between mill consumption poundage and end use poundage in any calendar year is seldom, if ever, obtained. The reasons for this, briefly stated, include (1) yarn and fabric inventory changes at all levels of the industry, (2) the incidence of the textile cycle, and (3) the fact that some items may be undermeasured, and certain items are not measured at all, in the survey.[25]

The end use consumption of wool, for example, consistently exceeds mill consumption. The double counting of wool occurs because the full possession losses are attributed to each individual end use in this study, and, also, unknown poundages of reused wool may be included.

An example: To produce a woman's finished skirt made of a five-count worsted yarn weighing one pound, it would be necessary to start out with about 1.35 pounds of raw wool at the top-making level to produce the garment. In this survey, the wool counted as being consumed in each skirt is 1.35 pounds, although it is known that the 0.35 pounds of wool "lost" in the initial spinning operation is later rerun in the manufacture of coarser count worsted—or woolen-spun yarns. These yarns are then used to produce other end-use products. It may be added that this same principle applies also to cotton, and, to a lesser extent, to man-made fibers.[26]

The table which follows shows that the total end-use consumption of textile fibers increased from 6,385 million pounds in 1956 to 7,093 million pounds in 1962. Increases were enjoyed for the same period in apparel, home furnishings, and other consumer-type prod-

---

25 *Textile Organon,* Vol. 34, No. 12, p. 187.
26 *Ibid.*

ucts and smaller amounts of textiles were used for industrial purposes or were exported. The percentage of total textile fiber consumption by end-use is given in Table 14.

TABLE XIV

End Use Consumption Summary For 101 Items

End Use & Year	Grand Total Lbs.	%	%	Cotton Lbs.	%	%	Wool Lbs.	%	%	Man-Made Fibers Lbs.	%	%
Total End Use Consumption												
1949-54 Av.	5934	100	100	3986	67.2	100	587	9.9	100	1361	22.9	100
1955-60 Av.	6437	100	100	4112	63.9	100	562	8.7	100	1763	27.4	100
1956	6385	100	100	4143	64.9	100	591	9.2	100	1651	25.9	100
1957	6305	100	100	4044	64.1	100	562	8.9	100	1699	27.0	100
1958	6179	100	100	3969	64.2	100	512	8.3	100	1698	27.5	100
1959	6788	100	100	4239	62.5	100	585	8.6	100	1964	28.9	100
1960	6627	100	100	4113	62.1	100	559	8.4	100	1955	29.5	100
1961	6647	100	100	4062	61.1	100	528	8.0	100	2057	30.9	100
1962	7093	100	100	4198	59.2	100	556	7.8	100	2339	33.0	100
Men's & Boys' Wear												
1949-54 Av.	1236	100	20.8	914	74.0	22.9	176	14.2	30.0	146	11.8	10.7
1955-60 Av.	1369	100	21.3	1035	75.6	25.2	181	13.2	32.2	153	11.2	8.7
1956	1376	100	21.6	1038	75.4	25.0	194	14.1	32.8	144	10.5	8.7
1957	1310	100	20.8	979	74.7	24.2	185	14.1	32.9	146	11.2	8.6
1958	1306	100	21.1	984	75.4	24.8	174	13.3	34.0	148	11.3	8.7
1959	1439	100	21.2	1091	75.8	25.7	181	12.6	31.0	167	11.6	8.5
1960	1431	100	21.6	1091	76.2	26.5	169	11.8	30.2	171	12.0	8.7
1961	1445	100	21.7	1093	75.6	26.9	154	10.7	29.2	198	13.7	9.6
1962	1559	100	22.0	1159	74.3	27.6	168	10.8	30.2	232	14.9	9.9
Women's, Misses' & Juniors' Wear												
1949-54 Av.	858	100	14.5	364	42.4	9.1	142	16.6	24.2	352	41.0	25.9
1955-60 Av.	991	100	15.4	482	48.6	11.7	157	15.9	28.0	352	35.5	19.9
1956	976	100	15.3	482	49.4	11.6	163	16.7	27.6	331	33.9	20.1
1957	1001	100	15.9	493	49.2	12.2	167	16.7	29.7	341	34.1	20.1
1958	975	100	15.8	481	49.3	12.1	146	15.0	28.5	348	35.7	20.5
1959	1039	100	15.3	498	47.9	11.8	161	15.5	27.5	380	36.6	19.3
1960	1016	100	15.3	466	45.9	11.3	156	15.3	27.9	394	38.8	20.1
1961	1029	100	15.5	447	43.4	11.0	155	15.1	29.3	427	41.5	20.8
1962	1095	100	15.4	457	41.8	10.9	168	15.3	30.2	470	42.9	20.1
Girls', Children's & Infants' Wear												
1949-54 Av.	292	100	4.9	231	79.1	5.8	29	9.9	4.9	32	11.0	2.4
1955-60 Av.	363	100	5.6	291	80.2	7.1	27	7.4	4.8	45	12.4	2.6
1956	351	100	5.5	280	79.8	6.8	29	8.2	4.9	42	12.0	2.5
1957	361	100	5.7	289	80.1	7.2	29	8.0	5.2	43	11.9	2.5
1958	357	100	5.8	290	81.2	7.3	24	6.7	4.7	43	12.1	2.5
1959	387	100	5.7	311	80.4	7.3	26	6.7	4.4	50	12.9	2.5
1960	383	100	5.8	307	80.2	7.5	25	6.5	4.5	51	13.3	2.6
1961	400	100	6.0	322	80.5	7.9	25	6.2	4.7	53	13.3	2.6
1962	423	100	6.0	337	79.7	8.0	26	6.1	4.7	60	14.2	2.6
Home Furnishings												
1949-54 Av.	1214	100	20.5	895	73.7	22.5	164	13.5	28.0	155	12.8	11.4
1955-60 Av.	1535	100	23.8	1008	65.7	24.5	155	10.1	27.6	372	24.2	21.1
1956	1502	100	23.5	1015	67.6	24.5	160	10.6	27.1	327	21.8	19.8
1957	1469	100	23.3	968	65.9	23.9	141	9.6	25.1	360	24.5	21.2
1958	1488	100	24.1	974	65.5	24.6	131	8.8	25.5	383	25.7	22.6
1959	1664	100	24.5	1055	63.4	24.9	178	10.7	30.4	431	25.9	22.0
1960	1649	100	24.9	1036	62.8	25.2	172	10.4	30.8	441	26.8	22.6
1961	1662	100	25.0	1011	60.9	24.9	157	9.4	29.7	494	29.7	24.0
1962	1805	100	25.5	1046	58.0	24.9	159	8.8	28.6	600	33.2	25.7
Other Consumer-Type Products												
1949-54 Av.	587	100	9.9	412	70.2	10.3	33	5.6	5.6	142	24.2	10.4
1955-60 Av.	623	100	9.7	403	64.7	9.8	26	4.1	4.6	177	28.4	11.0
1956	611	100	9.6	407	66.6	9.8	27	4.4	4.6	177	29.0	10.7
1957	603	100	9.6	395	65.5	9.8	26	4.3	4.6	182	30.2	10.7
1958	612	100	9.9	390	63.7	9.8	25	4.1	4.9	197	32.2	11.6
1959	650	100	9.6	399	61.4	9.4	24	3.7	4.1	227	34.9	11.6
1960	635	100	9.6	387	60.9	9.4	24	3.8	4.3	224	35.3	11.5
1961	640	100	9.6	375	58.6	9.2	23	3.6	4.4	242	37.8	11.7
1962	661	100	9.3	383	58.0	9.1	22	3.3	3.9	256	38.7	10.9

52

End Use & Year	Grand Total			Cotton			Wool			Man-Made Fibers		
	Lbs.	%	%	Lbs.	%	%	Lbs.	%	%	Lbs.	%	%
Industrial Uses												
1949-54 Av.	1348	100	22.7	876	65.0	22.0	39	2.9	6.6	433	32.1	31.8
1955-60 Av.	1240	100	19.3	663	53.5	16.1	13	1.0	2.3	564	45.5	32.0
1956	1261	100	19.7	703	55.8	17.0	15	1.2	2.5	543	43.0	32.9
1957	1213	100	19.2	664	54.7	16.4	12	1.0	2.1	537	44.3	31.6
1958	1122	100	18.1	608	54.2	15.3	10	0.9	2.0	504	44.9	29.7
1959	1298	100	19.1	656	50.5	15.5	12	0.9	2.1	630	48.6	32.1
1960	1202	100	18.1	604	50.3	14.7	10	0.8	1.8	588	48.9	30.1
1961	1174	100	17.7	600	51.1	14.8	11	0.9	2.1	563	48.0	27.4
1962	1249	100	17.6	599	48.0	14.3	11	0.9	2.0	639	51.1	27.3

End Use & Year	Grand Total			Cotton			Wool			Fibers		
	Lbs.	%	%	Lbs.	%	%	Lbs.	%	%	Lbs.	%	%
Exports of Domestic Products												
1949-54 Av.	399	100	6.7	294	73.7	7.4	4	1.0	0.7	101	25.3	7.4
1955-60 Av.	316	100	4.9	230	72.8	5.6	3	0.9	0.5	83	26.3	4.7
1956	308	100	4.8	218	70.8	5.3	3	1.0	0.5	87	28.2	5.3
1957	348	100	5.5	256	73.5	6.3	2	0.6	0.4	90	25.0	5.3
1958	319	100	5.2	242	75.9	6.1	2	0.6	0.4	75	23.5	4.4
1959	311	100	4.6	229	73.6	5.4	3	1.0	0.5	79	25.4	4.0
1960	311	100	4.7	222	71.4	5.4	3	1.0	0.5	86	27.6	4.4
1961	297	100	4.5	214	72.1	5.3	3	1.0	0.6	80	26.9	3.9
1962	301	100	4.2	217	72.1	5.2	2	0.7	0.4	82	27.2	3.5

Source: *Textile Organon*, Vol. 34, No. 12, Dec., 1963, pp. 176-177.

It may be noted in the following table that the amount of cotton consumed for industrial end-uses declined from 893.3 million pounds in 1949 to 599.2 in 1962. During the same period the consumption of wool for the same purpose dropped from 47.5 to 10.4 million pounds, while man-made fibers grew in popularity, increasing from 300 to 639.1 million pounds.

TABLE XV

Textile Fibers Consumed by Industrial End-Use by Individual Fiber, 1949-1962[27]

(in million pounds)

Year	Cotton	Wool	Man-Made
1949	893.3	47.5	300.0
1950	994.9	65.6	361.6
1951	1071.6	44.5	411.4
1952	836.7	32.2	503.3
1953	743.2	25.9	554.7
1954	698.4	17.8	457.4
1955	748.2	17.6	579.3
1956	703.6	14.7	543.0
1957	664.0	12.3	537.1
1958	608.3	10.0	504.0
1959	656.0	11.4	630.2
1960	604.3	10.2	587.8
1961	600.2	10.6	563.0
1962	599.2	10.4	639.1

[27] Data for years 1949 through 1956 obtained from *Textile Organon*, Vol. 32, No. 11 (Nov. 1961), p. 188; data for 1957-1962, *ibid.*, Vol. 34, No. 12 (Dec. 1963), p. 190.

Since its introduction in the United States the man-made fiber industry has enjoyed exceptional growth. By 1962 there were 98 plants distributed along the eastern part of the United States from Vermont to Florida, with over 66,000 employees. In the year 1962 more than $131,000,000 new capital was invested in plants for fiber production, and 2,242,500,000 pounds of man-made fiber was produced in this country. This was more than a fourth of the total man-made fiber production in all the countries of the world.[28]

Along with this great increase in production has been an expansion of the end-use of the fibers. This was made possible by the extensive research program which will doubtless continue to find additional markets for new and improved products, thus assuring the continuation of the expansion of this industry.

---

[28] *Man-Made Fiber Industry Fact Book,* pp. 2-6.

CHAPTER VI

Consolidations and Acquisitions

To establish mills in the South promoters needed only to obtain the backing of a few local citizens. Other funds were then available in loans from banks and manufacturers of machinery. The labor supply was large and, in general, the work required little skill. However, skilled employees such as work managers and mechanics were sometimes difficult to obtain. Under these conditions hundreds of small mills were established with communities endeavoring to out do each other in economic development. Community welfare rather than the profit motive was often emphasized.

While mills were larger in New England and not scattered over such a large area as in the South, they refrained from collective action. Many mills were known as "family mills" and were not receptive to changes; others were in the hands of trustees with the management ingrown.

With machinery standardized and with good markets, it was possible for the small mills to operate profitably during the last century. However, more recently, especially since World War I, there has been a decrease in the number and an increase in the size of cotton mills.

This movement was aided by the practices of some commission houses. Local capital was often limited and lacked merchandizing experience. Commission houses, therefore, helped finance mills and received in return exclusive rights to market the products of the mills. The small independent mills, unable to establish themselves as selling agents, were subject to control by the commission merchants. Often mill loans that could not be retired by current collections and sales of goods in stock were taken over by the merchants. Under such circumstances mills continued in operation but with no idea of providing profits to the stockholders. The commission merchants in such instances were satisfied with the usual commissions on sales, provided there were no losses on the operating end of the arrangements.[1] This relationship caused one writer to comment, "The (Commission) house is not run for the mill but the mill is run for the house."[2]

---

[1] C. T. Murchison, *Cotton is Sick*, p. 65.
[2] *American Wool and Cotton Reporter*, June 24, 1948, p. 47.

A number of mills controlled by single interests set up their own selling organizations. For example, the Cone Mills, engaged in making denims, coarse goods and other materials, established the Cone Export and Commission Company to serve as their selling agents. The Cannon Mills, makers of towels, yarns, sheetings and numerous other items, established their own selling houses to market their trademarked and nationally advertised commodities.

Other mills such as the Pacific Mills in 1929, and the Wamsutta Mills of New Bedford and the Nashua Manufacturing Company of Nashua, New Hampshire, in 1930 discontinued commission house connections and set up their own sales offices.[3]

Some selling organizations reversed this process by buying mills to support their sales. An important merger centering about converting and sales organizations was United Merchants and Manufacturers, Inc. Another group of mills sought to overcome defficiencies in industrial structure by creating their own cooperative selling organization, as, for example, the Southeastern Cottons, Inc.[4]

Increased integration was realized when mills were purchased by corporations which consume their products as raw material. The rubber tire manufacturers, for example, followed a policy of enlarging their own production of tire cord and fabric and, by 1930, approximately 75 per cent of this type of goods was produced in mills which were owned by the tire manufacturers.[5] The same trend toward the purchase of textile mills has been evident among surgical gauze, bag, coated fabrics, mop and shoe lining manufacturers.[6]

According to Stephen Jay Kennedy there were forty-three mergers and consolidations during the years 1919 through 1933. Of this number twenty-seven were horizontal in character—that is, mergers of two or more firms on the same level of production such as spinning, weaving, finishing and retailing establishments. Sixteen were along vertical lines, which involves the combination under one management of operating units in two or more stages in the manufacture and distribution of products.[7]

Despite the fact that $122,000,000 was involved in these consolidations, the number of mills in relation to the total number in the industry was small. It would appear, therefore, that the trend to-

  [3] C. T. Murchison, *Cotton is Sick*, pp. 174-178.
  [4] Solomon Barkin, "The Regional Significance of the Integration Movement in Southern Textile Industry," *Southern Economic Journal*, Vol. 15, p. 399.
  [5] C. T. Murchison, *Cotton is Sick*, p. 174.
  [6] H. S. Davis, G. W. Taylor, and Others, *Vertical Integration in the Textile Industries*, pp. 39-52.
  [7] *Profits and Losses in Textiles*, pp. 224-225, 231.

ward consolidation of small units into relatively large groups of mills had by the third decade of this century only begun to manifest itself in the cotton industry.

There was a let-up in consolidations in textiles following the great depression of the early 30's. Increased interest, however, in mergers began again in the following decade and reached a high peak as World War II ended. According to Cotton Textile Institute the ownership of about 154 cotton textile companies engaged in spinning and weaving, or both, changed in the period 1940-1946. These firms owned more than 4,400,000 spindles and more than 88,000 looms, or approximately one-fifth of the country's productive facilities.[8]

Writing in 1946, William B. Dall, Managing Editor of *Textile World*, stated that nearly twenty-five per cent of the cotton textile division had changed hands during the past two and one-half years, and noted that 145 cotton mill mergers and acquisitions had taken place between January 1, 1944 and July 1, 1946.[9]

About one-half the spindles that changed hands in the period 1940-1946 did so as a result of vertical integration while 18 per cent of the mergers were horizontal combinations. Many acquisitions of textile firms represented both types of integration.[10]

The two-way character of this merger movement may be noted in the case of Burlington Mills which, once basically a gray-goods manufacturer, moved into the finishing field, while Mr. Lowenstein and Sons, a converter, expanded backward acquiring gray-goods mills, and J. P. Stevens and Company, a leading sales agent, likewise extended itself backward by also purchasing gray-goods mills.[11]

The expansion of those three mills may be noted. Between 1940 and 1947 Burlington's purchases included Ranlo Manufacturing Company (Gastonia), Mid-State Cloth Mill (Statesville), Smithfield Manufacturing Company (Smithfield), Vamoco Mills (Franklinton), Robeson Textiles (St. Pauls), Steele Mills (Rockingham), Flint Manufacturing Company, Cramerton Textile Mills (Cramerton), Statesville Cotton Mills (Statesville), Sunspun Manufacturing Company (Ashboro), Arnco Finishing Corporation (Greensboro), in North Carolina and Everlastik, Inc. in Chelsea, Massachusetts.

[8] *Changes in American Textile Industry*, U. S. Dept. of Agri., Tech. Bull. 1210, p. 75.
[9] "Demand for Mills Affects Quarter of Industry," *Textile World*, July, 1946, pp. 101-104.
[10] *Changes in American Textile Industry*, U. S. Dept. of Agri., Tech. Bull. 1210, p. 76.
[11] *Ibid.*, p. 56.

M. Lowenstein and Sons during the years 1946 and 1947 bought controlling interest in the Huntsville Manufacturing Company of Alabama, Entwistle Manufacturing Company of Rockingham, North Carolina, Orr Mills in Anderson, South Carolina, and the Limestone and Hamrick Mills in Gaffney, South Carolina.

In 1946, J. P. Stevens absorbed eleven textile firms which controlled no less than thirty Southern and New England Mills. Additional purchases raised Steven's total spindles in cotton and rayon mills to nearly 631,000 in 1948 as compared with Burlington's 550,400 and Lowenstein's 336,100 spindles.[12]

Of the 117 mergers during the years 1948 to 1954, more than 37 per cent were acquisitions by firms with assets of fifty million dollars or more, and over 70 per cent were acquisitions by firms with assets of ten million dollars or more. The number of acquisitions per acquiring firm ranged from one to twelve companies. About 74 per cent of the companies purchased only one firm each, about fourteen per cent two firms each, and one company purchased as many as twelve firms.[13]

The greater concentration of the textile industry is indicated by reports that the share of the total spindles accounted for by the largest four textile companies increased from five per cent in 1937 to seventeen per cent in 1955. Cotton mills operated in 1954 by four of the largest of 278 companies accounted for fifteen per cent of the total number of employees and twenty-six per cent of the total value of the shipments of the industry. Mills operated by twenty of the largest companies, or less than eight per cent of the total number, accounted for forty-four per cent of the employees and fifty-six per cent of the value of shipments of the industry.[14]

Table XVI illustrates how leading textile companies expanded by way of merger, acquisition and internal growth during the decade 1950-1960.[15]

It may be noted that the twelve selected textile companies had 13.6 per cent of the textile sales for mill products in 1950 and that by 1960 this percentage had increased to 24.6 per cent.

No exact count has been kept of the consolidations and acquisitions in the textile industry but during the ten-year period, 1955-1964 the *Daily News Record* lists 748 such transactions. The trend has been toward larger corporations with control of all types of

---

[12] *Ibid.*, pp. 57-58.
[13] *Changes in American Textile Industry*, U. S. Dept. of Agri. Tech. Bull. 1210, p. 76.
[14] *Ibid.*, p. 77.
[15] *Patterns and Problems of Technical Innovation in American Industry*, Dept. of Comm., 1963, p. 15.

TABLE XVI

TEXTILE COMPANY EXPANSION, 1950-1960
(in $ million)

Year	Textile Mill Products	12 Selected Companies	Sales Concentration
1950	$12,725	$1,728.5	13.6%
1951	13,828	1,973.1	14.2
1952	12,673	2,026.8	16.0
1953	12,215	2,062.5	16.8
1954	11,401	1,924.8	16.9
1955	13,315	2,326.2	17.5
1956	13,018	2,690.5	20.6
1957	12,725	2,808.2	22.2
1958	11,864	2,662.3	22.5
1959	13,762	3,058.3	22.2
1960	13,254	3,257.3	24.6

production. An important change in this development has been the forward integration movement whereby mills, finishers and textile merchants have acquired independent converting operations. Some examples of tie-ups between converters and large textile companies on or before January 1, 1960, are (1) Burlington Industries, Inc. and Ely and Walker Dry Goods Company; (2) J. P. Stevens and Company–D. B. Fuller and Company; (3) Joseph Bancroft Sons Company–William Simpson Sons and Company; (4) Springs Mills, Inc.–Rollearre Fabrics, Inc.; (5) Cone Mills Corporation–Spinco Fabrics, Inc.; (6) Greenwood Mills, Inc.–Greenwood California Fabrics Corporation; (7) M. Lowenstein and Sons, Inc.–Pacific Mills Fabrics, Wamsutta Mills; and (8) United Merchants and Manufacturers–Bartuzen and Bixer, Inc.[16]

Reasons for acquisitions of mills are numerous; however, a few of the factors contributing to mergers in the industry may be mentioned. Profit margins affected by price control during World War II, expanded demand and pushed some mills to integrate forward by buying or building finishing plants to take advantage of higher margins on converted goods. This development led some converters and custom finishing plants to integrate backward by buying mills to secure a supply of goods for their finishing operations. Some selling houses bought mills in order to control a full line of products for sale. Various wholesale houses and mills that owned their own sales agencies integrated both backward and horizontally to control their sources of goods and to take advantage of higher margins.

---

[16] *Daily News Record,* Jan. 14, 1960, Sec. 2, p. 48.

Some firms which used yarns and fabrics in the manufacture of other products bought cotton mills to supply these materials.[17]

The solidification of the textile industry, through mergers, absorptions and consolidations has produced a stronger industry. In this process of integration selling agents, independent converters and commission merchants have lost a considerable amount of their traditional importance. Some companies now have full control from the mill to the retailer, and a few to the consumer. Such companies ordinarily spend more on advertising in order to establish brand names.

To meet consumers' demands, large integrated textile mills are engaged in multifiber operations producing in many instances a full line of textile fabrics and more mixed fabrics. Furthermore, the great growth in the size of the firms has made possible greater expenditures on research which in turn has created many new uses for textiles.

Diversification within the industry will doubtless continue with Burlington Industries, the world's largest textile organization leading the movement. This company now has 101 mills located in seventeen states, one in Puerto Rico, three in Canada, one in Colombia, two in France, three in Germany, three in Mexico, one in South Africa, one in Spain and six in Switzerland.[18]

Robert T. Stevens, President of J. P. Stevens and Company, has pointed out that the size and diversification of his company would not have been possible except through mergers and consolidations and he observed that the largest firm in the industry manufactures less than seven per cent of American textile production.[19]

It is thought, however, that some sales of mills were not consummated because of possible action by the Anti-Trust Division of the Department of Justice. Others point out that the buying trend will slow down because of the increase in the sale price of good plants, up thirty per cent since the advent of one-price cotton, and a decrease in the desire of coarse-yarn cloth weavers to sell their mills because of more favorable trade conditions.[20] Many observers feel, however, that the trend toward consolidation will continue for some years, but at a slower pace.

---

[17] Changes in American Textile Industry, U. S. Dept. of Agri., Tech. Bull. 1210, p. 76; see also Summary Rept. of the Federal Trade Commission on the Merger Movement, 1948, p. 55.
[18] Burlington Industries Annual Report, 1964.
[19] Daily News Record, Mar. 25, 1965, Section 2, p. 14.
[20] Ibid., p. 22.

CHAPTER VII

TEXTILE MACHINERY AND MILL MODERNIZATION

Textile Machinery

While textile machinery manufacturing companies were established in the United States over a century ago, it was not until the present century that the industry became interested in research. For example, Saco-Lowell in late thirties had a well-defined research department but it was not until 1959 that the company established an elaborate Research and Development Center on a thirty-acre tract at Clemson, South Carolina. And in 1951 Whitin Machine Works set up what is reputed to be the textile industry's largest research activity. It is housed in a building originally constructed as a cotton mill in 1847 but, recently renovated, it affords space for more than seventy persons to engage in demonstrating and testing, research and engineering activities. Approximately one hundred late-model textile machines are operated there and many tests run to help solve mill problems.

Other companies became interested in research activities, and between the end of World War II and 1957 the total expenditures on research and development and product improvement by American textile machine builders increased more than 200 percent. Expenditures in this area have continued to grow during more recent years.[1]

Results of these endeavors have been rewarding and numerous opportunities have been afforded executives of textile mills to examine the results of the research of textile machine manufacturing companies. At the Southern Textile Exposition in Greenville, South Carolina, in 1964, and at the American Textile Machinery Exhibition-International in Atlantic City, New Jersey, in 1965, hundreds of the most modern textile machines were on display.

Mildred B. Andrews' publication, *Profit Life of Textile Machinery* describes many textile machines and machine improvements and refinements throughout all phases of textile manufacture developed before 1957. Passing reference, therefore, will be made of only a few of the developments within the past decade.

In modern mills cotton now goes through a bale plucker and then through one cleaning point (in some instances two) then directly

---

[1] Mildred B. Andrews, *Profit Life of Textile Machinery*, p. 12.

to the cards by a chute feed. Due to the small tuft size, the blending is claimed to be four times as effective as that obtained from conventional opening lines. Therefore, a ten-bale mix on a modern opening line is the equivalent of 40 bales under the old system.

A number of advances have also been made in carding, and production rates in the range of forty to sixty pounds per hour are made possible by such attachments as the Crosol Web Purifier, Rola Kleen, Trashmasher and the Crosrol-Varga unit. These developments were accomplished because of the use of metallic card clothing which is receiving industry approval.[2]

The high speed rate carding creates more dust and fly on the cards and in the air. To alleviate this problem various cleaning systems have been introduced.

A number of improvements have been made within recent years in the drawing process. Automatic can changes have been developed by large can, high speed drawing frames. Modern draw frames operate at speeds of 800 feet per minute as compared with 200 feet a minute a decade ago. The draw boxes of the latest automated fiber handling process operate at speeds up to 1600 feet per minute, and some companies are considering manufacturing drawing frames that operate at production rates of about 2,000 to 2,500 feet per minute delivery speed, without loss of silver quality.

In roving, roll speeds have increased by about 50 per cent and flyer speeds have almost doubled. Newer frames operate at flyer speeds of over 1,000 revolutions per minute. A new builder screw and a new roving tension device increases production and allows more stock to be put into the roving package.[3]

Considerable advances have been made in spinning, and spindles speeds have increased to 15,000 revolutions per minute or about 30 to 40 per cent during the past decade. With recent advances in ring, traveler and spinning technology, it is estimated that in the near future spinning frames will operate at spindle speeds of over 18,000 revolutions per minute.

Automatic winding equipment producing cones or cheeses without the operation tieing in new packages or retrieving broken ends of already crated package is available. To maintain proper tension and catch gouts or slubs, electronic slub catchers have been developed. During the past decade winding and slashing have been increased about 50 per cent in speed.

[2] Jack Compton, "Trends in Textile Manufacture," *Southern Textile News,* Oct. 10, 1964, p. 5.
[3] *Ibid.,* p. 82.

Numerous improvements in recent years have been made in weaving machines. They include looms of 50 inches or more in width with speeds of 240 picks per minute, shutterless looms operating at speeds of 250 picks or higher per minute and circular looms weaving four fabrics at one time.

Through research by the industry during the past decade great advances have been made in automation. New mills and some conventional mills have capitalized upon some of the automated equipment being produced such as high speed cards, chute-fed cards, gang or railway carding arrangements, high speed drawing frames, new yarn spinning systems and automatic doffers.

Through the rapid development of more productive machinery a textile machinery manufacturing company pointed out that in 1960, a mill of 28,440 spindles with 19,456 additional feet of floor space was required to equal production of over 20,000 spindle mills in 1963.[4]

To supply the needs of the textile mills throughout the world, hundreds of textile machine manufacturing companies have been established in various countries. In 1965 more than 400 exhibitors, one-third from foreign countries, participated in the American Textile Machinery Exhibition-International in Atlantic City, New Jersey. Some idea of the growth of the textile machinery industry in the United States may be observed in Table XVII distributed by the American Textile Machinery Association.

It may be noted in this table that during the decade 1950 to 1960 the value of the exports of United States-built textile machinery far exceeded the value of foreign built imports to the United States. However, imports of foreign built textile machinery to the United States increased from $4,200,000 in 1950 to $27,400,000 in 1960 or over 600 per cent during the decade.

Mill Modernization

Many new mills have been constructed since World War II and many more will be built during this decade. They have been, and will be, built primarily for replacement rather than for expansion due to the increased cost of remodeling old buildings for new machinery, which has been estimated at about 80 to 85 per cent of the cost of building a new mill. The new mills are being so constructed that they can be expanded easily.

Practically all of the new plants are air conditioned with total air cleaning. The lint collecting feature of modern cleaning, there-

---

[4] *Saco-Lowell Bulletin, 150th Anniversary Issue,* p. 33.

TABLE XVII

TEXTILE MACHINERY SHIPMENTS IN $ VOLUME

Year	Total Shipments of U. S. Machine Builders (Includes Exports)	Foreign Built Imports To U. S. Mills	U. S. Built Textile Machinery Exports
1950	$456,000,000	$ 4,200,000	$ 99,600,000
1951	499,000,000	6,900,000	107,700,000
1952	368,000,000	6,100,000	78,600,000
1953	339,000,000	6,100,000	69,700,000
1954	304,000,000	8,000,000	71,800,000
1955	384,000,000	12,500,000	84,900,000
1956	407,000,000	16,500,000	86,000,000
1957	351,000,000	16,600,000	89,000,000
1958	322,000,000	12,500,000	65,000,000
1959	400,000,000	19,700,000	74,400,000
1960	500,000,000	27,400,000	113,800,000
1961	465,000,000	35,500,000	138,800,000
1962	532,427,000	39,900,000	132,000,000
1963	560,000,000	37,700,000	110,500,000
1964	644,000,000	52,400,000	137,900,000
1965	676,000,000	57,600,000	155,400,000
	(Estimated)	(Estimated)	(Estimated)

Source: Business and Defense Services Administration, Department of Commerce.

fore, combined with under floor return systems, makes cleaner mills, improves working conditions and increases production. But to realize the advantages of new technology companies must be strongly capitalized. Investment per employee in older plants averages between $6,000 and $10,000 per employee, but recently constructed plants represent an investment of $30,000 to $35,000, and it is estimated that mills currently under construction will cost about $50,000 per worker.

The industry has been rapidly modernized and automated. A survey made in 1958 showed that 77 per cent of the textile industry's plants and equipment was installed before the beginning of the Korean War. Three years later, a similar survey revealed that 49 per cent, or slightly less than one-half of the industry's capacity, was installed prior to the above stated time.[5]

Also, according to a McGraw-Hill survey, the textile industry devoted 5 per cent of its total capital investment for automated machinery and equipment in 1955. By 1959 it had increased to 9

---

[5] Douglas Greenwald, "Outlook for Textiles and Textile Machinery," speech at meeting of American Textile Machinery Association, Charlotte, N. C., Feb. 26, 1964.

per cent and by 1963 the amount going to automation had grown to 18 per cent of the total capital investment of the industry.[6]

The frequency of obsolescence in textile machinery is one of the determining factors in maintaining the high level of spending by many mills, while the liberalization of depreciation guidelines covering business outlays for new machinery and other capital, as put into effect during the present decade by the Federal Government, has proved helpful to modernization in the textile industry. However, the amount allowed is insufficient to meet the requirements of the developing industry, according to William E. Reid, President of Riegel Textile Corporation, who said, "The industry has brought us to a point where to put it bluntly, if a man doesn't plan to spend more than his depreciation and depletion allowance for new equipment, he may as well get out of textile manufacturing."[7]

The extent of the expenditures by the textile mills and other selected industries for new plants and equipment is noted in the following table.

TABLE XVIII

ANNUAL NEW PLANT AND EQUIPMENT EXPENDITURES
(in millions of dollars)

Year	All Industries	Manu- facturing Industries	Durable Goods	Non- durable Goods	Textile Mill Products	Paper and Allied Products	Chemicals and Allied Products
1949	19,285	7,149	2,594	4,555	471	298	670
1950	20,605	7,491	3,135	4,356	450	327	771
1951	25,644	10,852	5,168	5,684	531	420	1,247
1952	26,493	11,632	5,614	6,018	434	364	1,386
1953	28,322	11,908	5,648	6,260	378	409	1,130
1954	26,827	11,038	5,091	5,948	331	455	1,130
1955	28,701	11,439	5,436	6,003	366	518	1,016
1956	35,081	14,954	7,623	7,331	465	801	1,455
1957	36,962	15,959	8,022	7,937	408	811	1,724
1958	30,526	11,433	5,469	5,964	288	578	1,320
1959	32,543	12,067	5,773	6,294	412	630	1,235
1960	35,680	14,480	7,180	7,300	530	750	1,600
1961	34,370	13,680	6,270	7,400	500	680	1,620
1962	37,310	14,680	7,030	7,650	610	720	1,560
1963	39,220	15,690	7,850	7,840	640	720	1,610
1964	44,900	18,850	9,430	9,160	760	940	1,970
1965†	50,920	21,880	10,960	10,920	1,010	1,130	2,470

† Estimates are based on anticipated capital expenditures reported by business in late July and August 1965. Source: Securities and Exchange Commission; U. S. Department of Commerce.

---

[6] Ibid.

[7] Daily News Record, Jan. 21, 1965, p. 20.

It may be observed that the amount spent by the textile industry for new plants and equipment increased from $366,000,000 in 1955 to over $1 billion in 1965, or not quite 300 per cent. During the same period the percentage increase in expenditures by all industries, manufacturing industries, durable goods, non-durable goods, paper and allied products and chemicals and allied products was much less than that of textile mill products.

In 1965, Deering-Milliken, Incorporated, about three years later than Chemstrand Company, opened its Management Information Center in Spartanburg, South Carolina. This center is designed to automate and simplify the paper work and record keeping of the company's manufacturing, selling and affiliated organizations using a variety of communications. Detailed information from forty manufacturing and sales locations will be fed to the center, where it will be recorded by computers to provide statistical data and information for management action.

It is expected that this electronic system will provide facts from warehousing through manufacturing to sales, and even to projected sales. While full potential of the center may not be reached within the next year, counting and production monitoring devices have been helping to raise machine and work efficiency and productivity at Deering-Milliken.

In an address before the American Textile Machinery Association's textile management seminars, Mr. Charles F. Marshall, vice-president for engineering and construction, Springs Cotton Mills, Fort Mill, South Carolina, discussed the question of whether it was profitable to modernize an old mill building or to erect a new one. He pointed out that Springs Cotton Mills has committed $77 million for modernization and expansion in the past three years. Some new plants were constructed but the Springsteen plant in Chester, South Carolina was successfully remodeled. "This plant," he said, "is now operating and delivering goods that will match a new plant for quality. While the efficiency of this renovated plant cannot match that of a new plant, the efficiency achieved per dollar spent outstrips the new plant."[8]

In making a decision on whether to renovate an old mill or construct a new one, Mr. Marshall pointed out that (1) the trend to new mills is gathering momentum and the old mill's days are numbered; (2) each case of old mill *versus* new mill must be decided on its individual merits; (3) over-all cost, the time required to do the job, the length of payout and the availability of labor supply

---

[8] *Daily News Record,* Oct. 4, 1965, Sec. 1, p. 23.

are big factors; and (4) technological changes may drastically change the outlook for renovated plants.

It is contended that since modernization is a continuing process it might be better to modernize on a day-to-day basis rather than to make a major project of it. This procedure might insure general acceptance of the changes by the personnel involved. The personnel affected could also be more easily informed of expectations of any initial problems brought on by changes, as well as of the positive aspects of improved quality, better work flow and improved working conditions.

According to analysts of the Department of Commerce, plants in the textile industry with the highest productivity have spent most for plant and equipment. The work based on the 1958 census included only value added—that is, the value of finished production by various sized plants in the industry minus the cost of the original materials. This was reduced to an employee figure.

In tabulating productivity figures for the five industries, analysts divided plants in each industry into the top 25 per cent, the low 25 per cent, and the industry average.

TABLE XIX

COMPARISON OF MOST EFFICIENT PLANTS WITH LEAST EFFICIENT
PLANTS AND WITH INDUSTRY[9]

Industry	Industry Average	Most Efficient	Least Efficient	Ratios Most Eff. Least Efficient	Most Eff. Industry Average
Cotton Weaving Mills	$4,400	$6,600	$2,700	2.4	1.5
Synthetic Weaving Mills	5,700	9,800	3,300	2.9	1.7
Wool weaving finish mills	6,000	9,500	3,300	2.9	1.6
Narrow fabric mills	5,800	8,800	3,500	2.5	1.5

Capital Expenditure per Employee					
Cotton weaving mills	$ 200	$ 220	$ 150	1.4	1.1
Synthetic weaving mills	180	200	140	1.5	1.1
Wool weaving finish mills	170	220	150	1.5	1.3
Narrow fabric mills	260	360	240	1.8	1.4
Seamless hosiery mills	200	270	60	4.5	1.4

It may be noted that the value added by employees in the cotton weaving mills industry was $4,400. Plants in the top 25 per cent have a value added of $6,600, while plants in the lower 25 per cent have $2,700 added value.

---

[9] *Ibid.*, p. 17; U. S. Dept. of Comm., *U. S. Industrial Outlook 1966*, p. 211.

Plants in the top 25 per cent have a ratio of 2.4 times as much value added per employee as the plants in the bottom 25 per cent and 1.5 times more than the industry average.

It would seem, therefore, that the added investment in modernizing the textile industry in the United States not only keeps it competitive with the textile industry in other countries of the world but also yields financial gains. The textile industry, however, to some extent, always has been automated, but within recent years the research by textile companies and machinery manufacturers have resulted in remarkable advances in automated manufacturing processes. Further advancement is anticipated in the near future, such as higher speeds in processing raw materials, the elimination of roving, ringless spinning, higher speeds in weaving, increased automation, especially in high cost areas like spinning, mechanical cloth inspection and improvements in sewing machines and apparel-making techniques.

CHAPTER VIII

TEXTILE EDUCATION

The United States lagged behind European countries in introducing textile education largely because American mills manufactured coarse and medium goods of simple design. However, with the movement for industrial drawing and manual training in the public schools of Massachusetts came the desire for more adequate training in industrial design. As a result the Lowell School of Practical Design was established in 1872 for instruction in textile design, followed by the Rhode Island School of Design founded in Providence in 1878[1]

Philadelphia College of Textiles and Science

The first textile school in the United States giving general instruction in textile work was established in Philadelphia in 1884 by the Philadelphia Manufacturers Association. While this institution was equipped by the manufacturers of Philadelphia, the State of Pennsylvania contributed to its support.[2] At first known as the Philadelphia Textile School, its name was changed in 1941 and since 1960 it has been known as the Philadelphia College of Textiles and Science. The college moved to a new campus in 1949 and all buildings except the administration building have been built since that time.

In 1943 the work of the college was expanded to enable it to award a Bachelor of Science degree and in 1955 it was accredited by the Middle States Association of Colleges.

Six curricula are presently offered leading to the Bachelor of Science degree: Textile Engineering, Chemistry and Dyeing, Textile Management and Marketing, Fabric Design, Business Administration, and Chemistry. The latter two offer textiles as electives.

The number of graduates by years for the past ten years are as follows: 1955—71, 1956—68, 1957—78, 1958—82, 1959—71, 1960—83, 1961—72, 1962—66, 1963—63 and 1964—115. With an enrollment in 1964 of about 750 students, the college plans to expand to approximately 1500 students. Scheduled for addition in the near future is an apparel research center.

---

[1] U. S. Dept. of Lab., Bull. No. 54 (1904), p. 1379.
[2] *Ibid.*

69

Three City Schools

New England cotton manufacturers in an effort to develop the manufacture of finer grades of cotton goods in the area promoted the development of textile schools. Largely through their efforts a law was passed in Massachusetts in 1895 authorizing the establishment of a textile school in any city in the state which had at least 450,000 spindles. It provided state aid of $25,000 if the municipality raised an equal amount. Four cities, Lowell, Fall River, New Bedford and Lawrence, had the required number of spindles and all established schools except Lawrence which, being near Lowell, helped to support that school instead of establishing one of its own.

New Bedford Institute of Technology

The New Bedford Institute of Technology was founded in 1895, and in 1897 the city of New Bedford appropriated $25,000 to match a like sum appropriated by the state of Massachusetts. This fund was used to erect a school building and equipment was given by persons interested in textiles. During the early period of the institution instruction was given in the theory and practice of the various phases of manufacturing, finishing and distribution of textiles. More recently the curriculum was expanded to include other forms of technology. It is presently accredited by the New England Association of Colleges, and the Collegiate Board of Authority of Massachusetts has authorized it to confer not only the Bachelor of Science degree but also the Master of Science degree in Textile Technology and Textile Chemistry.

The number of graduates receiving the Bachelor of Science degree in a textile major program during the past decade were as follows: 1955—29, 1956—34, 1957—33, 1958—31, 1959—38, 1960—44, 1961—30, 1962—40, 1963—33, and 1964—31.

Bradford Durfee College of Technology

Bradford Durfee College of Technology was incorporated in 1899 and, as in the case of the New Bedford Institute of Technology, state funds were matched to build the school. The school was opened in 1904 and instruction was offered to those who wished preliminary training in manufacturing processes before going to work in the mill, and to operatives employed in a mill who desired to upgrade themselves through evening courses.

Until 1918 the school was supported entirely by the city of Fall River at which time it became strictly a state institution. The city

70

of Fall River, however, continued its interest in the school and annually contributed $10,000 to help defray the cost of operation.

In the early period cotton manufacturing was emphasized, and a three-year diploma course and two two-year certificate courses, one in textile design and weaving, the other in chemistry and dyeing, were offered.

During the years which followed various courses were added, and in 1946 the name of the school was changed to Bradford Durfee Technical Institute. Finally, in 1948, the Board of Collegiate Authority of Massachusetts authorized the institution to award the Bachelor of Science degree.

To indicate a further expansion in the programs offered, the name of the institution underwent greater change to become Bradford Durfee College of Technology, and in 1961 it was accredited by the New England Association of Colleges and Secondary Schools. The average number of textile graduates per year during the past decade has been between twelve and fifteen with the enrollment in this division increasing each year.

On July 1, 1964, the New Bedford Institute of Technology merged with the Bradford Durfee College of Technology into the Southeastern Massachusetts Technological Institute. A new campus, under construction in North Dartmouth, is approximately mid-way between New Bedford and Fall River. The first complex of buildings opened in 1965 and absorption of the New Bedford and the Fall River facilities is expected in 1966 or 1967.

Textile studies will, of course, be included in the greatly expanded offerings of the Southeastern Massachusetts Technological Institute with Bachelor of Science and Master of Science degrees being granted in textile chemistry and textile technology.

Massachusetts Institute of Technology

Textile education was formally begun at the Massachusetts Institute of Technology in 1872 and this design course was transferred to the Boston Museum of Fine Arts in 1903. As early as 1883 however, mechanical engineering students were given courses in the design of textile machinery and of textile mills.

In 1885 a textile engineering option was included in the course leading to the Bachelor of Science degree in Mechanical Engineering. Later this option was modified to give increased emphasis on modern concepts of textile-technology. In 1927 additional courses were added to the curriculum and graduate work was offered leading to the Master of Science degree. By 1964 seventy such degrees had been conferred.

Massachusetts Institute of Technology also offers work leading to the degree of Doctor of Science in Mechanical Engineering and has awarded seven such degrees.

The formal textile courses utilize the students' background in classical subjects and emphasize the most recent applications of engineering and scientific fundamentals to textile engineering. Emphasis is placed on the applied mechanics of textile structures, on the rheology of fibrous materials, and on the dynamics and mechanisms of textile processing.

The Textile Division has also extended its educational influence through the medium of summer courses and special research symposia. The program, begun in 1929, enjoys the interest of the textile industry, thus has justified frequent presentations of varied program material relating to fiber science and textile engineering.

A. French Textile School

The General Assembly of Georgia, having noted the need for trained personnel in the textile industry in the state, appropriated, in December, 1897, $10,000 for the establishment of a textile department at the Georgia Institute of Technology. This appropriation, however, was made on condition that the school match funds with an equivalent amount of money and machinery. The response was good, and in 1898 nearly $20,000 worth of machinery and about $13,500 in cash were donated.

The school was named in honor of Mr. Aaron French, who cooperated personally and financially in meeting the conditions imposed by the legislature. Instruction in textiles and textile engineering began in 1899 and the first two graduates finished in 1901 with the degree of Bachelor of Science in Textile Engineering.

In 1949 a new building was erected to house the textile school. This structure was made possible by an appropriation of approximately a million dollars by the state legislature; and more than $350,000 was provided for new machinery by the Textile Education Foundation of the Cotton Manufacturers Association of Georgia. This Foundation also contributed over $500,000 to further the study of textiles at the A. French Textile School of the Georgia Institute of Technology.

Prior to 1949 the single degree was used for all graduates despite the growing specialization in the textile industry. In 1949 two degrees were established, Bachelor of Textile Engineering and Bachelor of Science in Textiles. A third degree, Bachelor of Science in Textile Chemistry, was added to the curriculum in 1960.

72

The first degree in the graduate program was granted in 1930 and since then 72 Masters degrees have been conferred.

Basic and sponsored research has been carried on in the school since its founding. Some of this work has been done individually, but much of it was done in conjunction with the Engineering Experiment Station and other schools of the Georgia Institute of Technology.

The student enrollment in the A. French Textile School for the academic year 1964-65 was 180, and the number graduating by years were: 1955—59, 1956—42, 1957—49, 1958—47, 1959—49, 1960—34, 1961—38, 1962—26, 1963—43 and 1964—38.

The school plans to continue its emphasis on the engineering aspects of textiles and the interdisciplinary work in research.

Clemson University

The Textile School at Clemson University was opened in 1898 and through 1920 the textile course was entitled "Textile Industry." In 1921 the course was changed to "Textile Engineering" and continued as such until the general curriculum change in 1957. In 1931 the major in "Textile Chemistry" was begun and has continued to the present time.

A new textile building, built as a P.W.A. project at a cost of about $485,000, was occupied in 1938. Shortly thereafter the South Carolina Legislature voted $50,000 for equipment, which was matched by another $50,000 by the mills of South Carolina. World War II interfered with the spending of these funds, and it was not until 1947 that the new equipment was purchased. In 1950 about $300,000 was made available to the school for additional equipment.

In 1949 a graduate program in Textile Chemistry was initiated offering the Master of Science degree.

Until 1925 the number of graduates in the Textile School never exceeded 20 and generally numbered about 10, with no graduates in 1908 and 1909. The graduating class reached a high of 30 in 1925 and 1934 and an all time high before World War II of 88 in 1941.

After World War II there was a great increase in the enrollment in the School of Textiles and 216 degrees were awarded in 1950. The number of Bachelor of Science degrees awarded the following years were 1954—116, 1955—113, 1956—115, 1957—107, 1958—74, 1960—56, 1961—44, 1962—55, 1963—51, 1964—57. During the period 1960 to 1964, eleven Master of Science degrees were conferred.

While there has been a certain amount of research work at the School of Textiles since it was established, it was not until 1958 that the Textile Research Department of the School of Textiles was formally established. Much of the work by this department is sponsored research, but it is hoped that an increasing amount of original research will be possible in the future.

The textile industry of South Carolina has contributed about one million dollars to what is now known as the J. E. Sirrine Textile Foundation which has been, and is, assisting the School of Textiles of Clemson University in many ways.

School of Textiles of North Carolina State University

Textile education began at North Carolina State College in 1899 and in 1901 moved into a new building made possible by a $10,000 appropriation by the state legislature. Both the staff and student body increased in size.

The first public recognition came in 1907, when the Jury of Awards of the Jamestown Tercentennial conferred a gold medal on the Textile Department for fabrics designed and woven by the students of this school.

In March, 1914, the textile building and much of its equipment was destroyed by fire, but within three years the building was reconstructed and new equipment was in place, much of which was donated or purchased at cost. By 1919, the department had a staff of five members and an enrollment of 154 students.

In 1929 the Department was removed from the School of Engineering and a Textile School established. Finally the legislature of North Carolina, in 1937, appropriated $45,000 for building expansion but the administration decided to await further developments. Two years later a new textile building was erected as a W.P.A. project.

In 1942, the North Carolina Textile Foundation was incorporated "to aid and promote by financial assistance and otherwise, all types of textile education and research at North Carolina State College." By 1964 this Foundation had contributed over $2,000,000 to the School of Textiles.

Research activities at North Carolina School of Textiles began in a small way in 1944. The legislature of North Carolina made its first appropriation of $80,000 for basic textile research. Since then the total appropriated by the state legislature for research purposes exceeds $780,000.

The school offers the Master of Science degree in Textile Technology and Textile Chemistry as well as the professional degree of Master of Textile Technology. It also has a working arrangement with various departments of North Carolina State University, such as chemistry, physics, chemical and mechanical engineering, whereby graduate students may carry out research on textile problems under guidance of the School of Textile faculty with the Doctor of Philosophy degree being conferred in the appropriate discipline of the cooperating department.

The number of Bachelor of Science degrees conferred by years during the past decade are 1955—108, 1956—95, 1957—106, 1958—98, 1959—86, 1960—62, 1961—94, 1962—80, 1963—83 and 1964—117. During the ten-year period seventy-four Master of Science degrees were awarded, 11 in 1964, and 14 in 1963.

The enrollment in the School of Textiles for the school year 1964-65 was 603, the highest since 1950 when many veterans of World War II were enrolled.

School of Textile Technology, Auburn University

The School of Textile Technology, established at Auburn University in 1928, was first called the School of Textile Engineering and occupied the present Textile Building in 1930. By 1932, when the first degree was awarded, seventy-one students were enrolled in the school.

In 1954 the Alabama Textile Education Foundation was organized by the Alabama Textile Manufacturers Association to assist the School of Textile Technology. To date, this Foundation not only has contributed over $100,000 in support of the school, but its cooperation has resulted in the school's receiving gifts of machinery and equipment valued at approximately $250,000.

In 1953 a two-year certificate course was introduced to fulfill the need of industry for men with some advanced training for sub-supervisors.

Two courses of study, Textile Science and Textile Management, are offered for degrees, and during the past decade the following number of students have been graduated: 1955—13, 1956—22, 1957—16, 1958—30, 1959—32, 1960—22, 1961—16, 1962—17, 1963—16 and 1964—15.

Textile Research Institute

Textile Research Institute was founded in 1930 as a nonprofit membership corporation of New York state. The original name was United States Institute for Textile Research, but the name was changed to Textile Research Institute in 1941. The Institute was incorporated in New Jersey as a nonprofit institution of learning in June 1951.

The cooperative educational program with Princeton University which began in 1944 provides for qualified Bachelor degree chemists and engineers to pursue, as T.R.I. predoctoral fellows, graduate studies leading to the Ph.D. degree from Princeton University. While the students take the regular graduate course of studies at Princeton, their doctoral dissertation research is conducted under Princeton faculty supervision in the T.R.I. laboratories on subjects relating to fibers. About twenty-five research fellows have received the Ph.D. degree within the past ten years.

The institute has a postdoctoral program for persons seeking to carry on special research in textiles. Postdoctoral fellows work on a full-time basis and appointments are usually for one year, but may be extended under special circumstances. Appointees are not affiliated with, but may use the facilities of, Princeton University.

The prime purpose of the Institute is technological advancement in textile and allied fields. Research has been carried on in this area for industry, Government agencies and other organizations, and the findings published in various scientific journals. Financial support for the program comes from individuals and organizations interested in general development of the textile industry.

Institute of Textile Technology

Twenty-three textile executives met in April, 1944, and signed the charter of the Institute of Textile Technology now located at Charlottesville, Virginia. As stated in the charter, the principal objectives of the Institute are: 1. to conduct research on textile raw materials, products and processes; 2. to maintain a library and information service to keep mills abreast of developments in the textile industry throughout the world; and 3. to train at graduate level in the fundamental sciences and in textile technology.

The Institute's project research, which belongs to the entire membership, is the outgrowth of needs developed at meetings of the Technical Advisory Committee, suggested by representatives of member companies or by the staff of the Institute. These projects usually cover the areas of mill processing, raw materials, wet processing, instrumentation, statistical quality control, chemical treatment, industrial engineering, systems development or testing.

The Institute also works on short term problems submitted to it by member firms. Fifteen per cent of the dues paid by each member is set aside for that purpose. These problems include, among others, time study, work assignments, design of mill experiments, the blending of raw materials, new machinery evaluation, new product

76

research, customer complaints, product quality, sampling techniques, selection of raw materials, assistance in mill research, and evaluation of data. Findings in these studies are often used as case histories in classroom discussion, thus affording students an insight into the daily problems that arise in textile manufacturing.

The program of graduate studies which began in 1947 was designed to give a broad training in the sciences, experience in the conduct of research and a knowledge of textile technology. Assistance is given in various subjects such as mechanical and civil engineering by professors from the University of Virginia.

The Institute has awarded over one hundred Master of Science degrees and two Doctor of Philosophy degrees. The results of thesis research, required for these degrees, have benefitted member companies, for since 1951 the thesis problems have been a part of regular Institute Research Projects. Thus data has been made available which otherwise might not have been obtained.

The Library of the Institute has an extensive collection of magazines, journals, books, trade literature and the like which cover important periods of development of textile history. Much of this material has been, and current material is being, abstracted monthly and published as the *Textile Technology Digest* for interested readers.

Lowell Technological Institute

Lowell Technological Institute is located in Lowell, Massachusetts. Included among other degrees awarded at this institution are the Bachelor of Science degree in Textile Engineering and Bachelor of Science and Master of Science degrees in Textile Chemistry and Textile Technology. It is a state-controlled school. The facilities of the Lowell Technological Institute Research Foundation are available to the Institute.

Texas Technological College

Texas Technological College, located in Lubbock, awards Bachelor of Science degrees in Textile Engineering and Textile Technology and Management. From 1954 through 1964 twenty-six degrees in Textile Engineering and two degrees in Technology and Management were awarded. It is a state college and has received some assistance from the textile industry.

The textile research laboratories of the college are available to both private and public agencies for research in cotton utilization and textile manufacturing problems.

Design Schools

Mention should doubtless be made of three other schools: (1) the Fashion Institute of Technology, New York City, which includes in its offerings courses in textile administration and sales, textile and pattern drafting and design, and fashion buying and merchandizing; the New York-Phoenix School of Design, New York City, which gives three year courses in textile design, advertising design, fashion illustration and in other subjects; and (3) the Rhode Island School of Design, Providence, where emphasis is placed on the study of textile designs and related areas.

Scholarships

Doubtless all of the textile schools award scholarships and make available financial assistance to worthy and needy students. For example, for the year 1964-65, Southern Massachusetts Technological Institute awarded 28 scholarships varying in amounts between $100 and $250 for a total of $6,700. Clemson University awarded 37 undergraduate scholarships with a monetary value of $19,350 and a range in amounts between $250 to $750. 122 grants of the School of Textiles North Carolina State University ranged between $175 and $4,000 for an average per scholarship of $625. The A. French Textile School at Georgia Institute of Technology awarded 43 undergraduate scholarships of between $250 and $1000, and 7 graduate fellowships of $1000 to $3600 in amount for total value respectively of $24,500 and $14,400. The Philadelphia College of Textiles and Science extended grants ranging between $100 and $900 to 42 students for a total amount of $20,175. The Institute of Textile Technology awarded 17 fellowship grants each for $2,500. Grants at the Massachusetts Institute of Technology run from $5000 upward for graduate students. The fellowship stipends at the Textile Research Institute at Princeton, New Jersey, are $2,200 for graduate students who have not taken the general examinations, and $2,500 for those who have passed them, plus regular graduate school tuition fees at Princeton University.

In addition to the above-mentioned grants are numerous scholarships given by textile executives or companies to able students. Various loan funds have also been established at the educational institutions where needy students may obtain loans at most reasonable terms.

Vocational Education

Vocational education courses were given in night schools at various cotton mills during the first years of this century. The early efforts were supported by mills but later cooperative arrangements were made between mills and the government with mills supplying space, equipment and materials for classes.

With the passage of the Smith-Hughes Act in 1917[3] a broad program for vocational education was initiated in the United States. The Act provides "that for each dollar of Federal money expended . . . the state or local community or both shall expend an equal amount." The George-Dean Act of 1936[4] aided in the same field of endeavor but required matching funds in the program of the secondary school level only to the extent of 50 per cent of the Federal funds each year until 1942, and then 10 per cent additional each year thereafter until a maximum of 100 per cent matching was required. The George-Barden Act of 1946 replaced the George-Dean Act and contained the basic provisions of providing funds for vocational education in trades and industry.

The National Defense Education Act of 1958, commonly referred to as Public Law 864, provides, among other things, funds to states for allocation to local school districts to encourage the development of vocational education programs.

The textile mills have benefitted from the work carried on by federal-state cooperation in vocational education and have furnished places for classes to meet under the program and have given materials and equipment for classroom work. The program has included studies in mill arithmetic, foremanship, loom fixing and other subjects relating to the industry.

State action in vocational education has been taken. In 1943, the North Carolina Vocational Textile School was opened near Belmont. The Legislature of North Carolina in 1941 appropriated $50,000 for the establishment of the school which the textile industry of Gaston County supplemented with $50,000. The building site was given by industries in Belmont, as well as $1,600 for beautification of the grounds. Later appropriations were made by the legislature in support of the school.

The North Carolina Vocational Textile School in Gastonia has also been most helpful in training personnel for the textile industry.

Technical Education Centers in South Carolina

The General Assembly of South Carolina in 1961 made possible a program of increased technical training through the formation of Technical Education Centers. The Legislative Act provided for

[3] 39 *Stat.* 929-936.
[4] 49 *Stat.* 1488-1490.

the establishment of a committee including one representative from each of South Carolina's congressional districts and two *ex officio* members, the State Superintendent of Education, and the director of the State Development Board. Several centers have been approved and were built as community do-it-yourself projects with the region served providing the construction funds and a part of the operating budget. Course offerings at all centers provide three district avenues of learning—Technician, Trade and Up-Dating and Up-Grading courses.

The center established at Greenville was the first Technical Center constructed in South Carolina. The Textile Technology Department expanded in 1965 into a new building which contains a textile manufacturing laboratory, textile testing laboratory, textile dyeing and finishing laboratory, inorganic chemistry laboratories, organic chemistry laboratories, instrumentation laboratory, chemical instrumentation laboratory and other related laboratories. The Center uses the latest textile manufacturing, textile finishing and chemical related equipment in the instructional program.

The Center is co-educational and students must be eighteen years of age or high school graduates. Technician level students are required to possess the qualities and maturity of high school graduates and to have completed two years of mathematics including one year of Algebra. Physics and chemistry are also desirable prerequisites for students of technology.

Textile Technology is a two-year course at the Greenville Center where students study textiles from raw material to the finished product. Included in the offerings are the following courses: Yarn Manufacturing, Textile Chemistry and Dyeing, Fabric Design, Weaving, Textile Testing, Synthetic Fibers, Statistical Control, Cost Analysis, Plant Organization and Textile Finishing.

This Technical Education Center offers the Associate of Science degree in Textile Chemistry and also in Textile Manufacturing.

Industrial Education Centers in North Carolina

Vocational education has been developed in one way or another throughout the United States. Brief mention of its development in North Carolina will be made. Vocational education, better known as trade and industrial education, has been provided in the public schools of the state for some decades but has in general been limited to schools in large urban centers. But neither this nor training on-the-job programs offered by many mills met the needs of the times. Therefore, in 1957 challenge funds were made available

80

by the General Assembly. Once a Center was approved for an area, the community provided the site and building. In 1959 the General Assembly officially authorized a vocational school known as an "Industrial Education Center" conducted for adults as well as mature or select high school students. The legislature also approved an appropriation requested by the State Board of Education for the operation of existing and proposed programs in the Centers.

The major areas taught at the Industrial Education Centers are courses for machine operators, craftsmen, technicians, supervisory personnel and updating classes for employed adults.

The largest enrollment in the Centers has been among adults who are upgrading their present job skills or taking training for additional skill. In 1962, 6,595 students were enrolled in a curriculum type program in the twenty centers, and 18,971 in the extension classes. A portion of this number sought employment in the textile industry of North Carolina.

Summary

While the first textile schools gave instruction in designing in the 1870's before the end of the century institutions giving instruction in all the various processes connected with the manufacture of textiles were established. These schools, distributed over a wide area from Massachusetts to Alabama, are mostly supported by public funds but also enjoy financial assistance from the industry. Because of this support these institutions have progressed, and today American textile schools are the best in the world.

To instruct operatives in their work in the textile mills, on-the-job training programs were introduced in many plants. However, to meet the increased demands for skilled labor, federal and state legislation was passed to expand the vocational education program. While progress in this program during the past decade has been enjoyed in the whole of the United States, comment in this chapter was limited to its development in North and South Carolina.

CHAPTER IX

RESEARCH AND DEVELOPMENT

It is obvious to even the casual observer that the textile industry has undergone great changes. For example, in 1930 there were a little over 31 million active cotton spindles for the needs of 123 million people while in 1964 approximately 18 million spindles met the demands of over 190 million people. The increased productivity of labor during this period was largely due to improved machinery.

Shortly after World War I the results of research by industries became apparent, but the textile industry was late in arriving at a decision as to what course to follow. Marketing of cotton goods was a problem and there was clamor to extend the market for cotton goods by finding new uses. There were, however, no over-all plans for a program of research for the improvement of the industry. The first laboratories for the study of fiber manipulation and processing machinery were started independently by the United States Rubber Company and jointly by the Pacific Mills and Lockwood, Greene and Company. Other tire manufacturers organized textile research laboratories concerned primarily with the development of better yarns or fabrics to be made on existing equipment for tires and rubber goods. When Lockwood, Greene and Company withdrew, the Pacific Mills found that a laboratory devoted to the study of textile processes was too expensive for a single mill to handle. As many others felt the same way, the study of research in cotton was neglected for many years.[1] In the 1930's basic research got vocal attention but little monetary support. Because new constructions of cloth received little or no patent protection and were easily pirated, the mills concentrated on the reduction of costs.

A number of research and development companies were established but confined their efforts largely to job assignments of the workers. As a result of these efforts the textile industry enjoys greater job standardization with fewer unprofitable man-hours than many other industries.[2] By 1940 some thirteen companies were engaged in research in cotton and cotton products and 163 companies were engaged in textile research. By 1946 the number had

---

[1] Peter M. Strange, "Review of Textile Research," *America's Textile Reporter*, January 26, 1961, p. 21.
[2] *Ibid.*, p. 22.

increased to 27 in cotton products while 258 companies had research laboratories devoted in whole or in part to work in textiles and related subjects.[3]

Textile research workers in 1940 totaled 1575, of whom 806 were professionally trained; and by 1946 the number had increased to 3,175, of which 1,280 were chemists, engineers and others having professional training. Included in the 3,175 were 536 persons engaged in cotton research of whom 226 were professional personnel. The others devoted their attention to rayon, fiberglas, wool and nylon.[4] The textile industry spent nearly $16,000,000 in research in 1946 as compared with $8,000,000 in 1940.

Nevertheless in 1946 the textile industry was still far behind most other industries in size and scope of its research effort. The 3,175 textile research workers was only 2.4 per cent of the aggregate of 133,515 for American industry. Moreover most of the research work was concentrated in companies which produced rayon and other man-made fibers.[5]

It may be noted that the textile industry developed through the last century without formalized research. Traditionally the industry has been made up of small units only a very few of which could afford expensive laboratories. Low profits in the industry have not encouraged research expenditure, and within recent years textile spending on research and development, as a per cent of profits, has been below average. The record of research and development expenditures in textiles and in all manufacturing industry from 1953 through 1959 is included in the following table.

TABLE XX

RESEARCH AND DEVELOPMENT EXPENDITURES, TEXTILES
AND ALL MANUFACTURING, 1953-59[6]

(in millions)

| | | Textiles | | | All manufacturing | |
Year	Profits	R. & D. expenditures	R. & D. as percent of aftertax profits	Profits	R. & D. expenditures	R. & D. as percent of aftertax profits
1953	$286	$26	9.1	$11,340	$3,314	29.2
1954	114	33	28.9	11,232	3,711	33.0
1955	346	33	9.5	15,099	4,514	29.9
1956	342	33	9.6	16,153	5,786	35.8
1957	253	37	14.6	15,438	6,935	44.9
1958	189	34	18.0	12,670	7,818	61.7
1959	416	35	8.4	16,328	8,656	53.0

[3] "Industrial Research Laboratories of the United States," *Bulletin of the National Research Council*, No. 113, July 1946, and No. 104, Dec., 1940.
[4] *Ibid.*, 1946.
[5] Joseph V. Sherman, "Textile Research Shows Rapid Growth," *Textile World*, Jan., 1947, p. 204.
[6] Supp. Rept. of Com. on Comm., No. 173, 87th Cong., 1st Sess., p. 9.

The loss of export trade due to world competition plus, the loss in traditional markets to nontextile substitutes, such as paper, pointed to the need for expanded research to discover additional uses for cotton commodities. Some idea of the relative position of textiles in research and development in 1959 may be noted in the table below.

TABLE XXI

EXPENDITURES BY INDUSTRIES ON RESEARCH AND DEVELOPMENT IN 1959[7]

Industry	Millions
Aircraft	3,250.3
Electrical Equipment	1,607.9
Machinery	678.0
Chemicals	661.8
Professional and Scientific Instruments	382.9
Petroleum	300.7
Fabricated Metals	223.0
Primary Metals	138.1
Food	99.2
Rubber	89.3
Stone, clay, glass	73.6
Paper	63.4
Textiles and Apparel	34.6
Other manufacturing	1,055.6
Nonmanufacturing	370.6
TOTAL	9,027.0

There is no record of the amount the textile industry spent on capital equipment for research purposes, but it doubtless amounted to at least 60 per cent of the total cost of research. Personnel costs increased. The textile industry in 1951 spent between $10,000 and $20,000 per research scientist or engineer, but by 1956 the industry average in larger firms had increased to about $36,000.[8]

The industry realized the need for advancement of the research program and during the latter part of the 1950's some progress was realized. There was a real problem, however, of how to finance an extensive research program in the face of dwindling earnings. The Committee on Interstate and Foreign Commerce of the United States Senate, after investigating the problems of the domestic textile industry, made the following recommendations:

> We recommend that some proportion of certain duties collected on textile products entering the United States be used to finance research—especially basic research

---

[7] C. S. McKean, "Can Textiles Catch Up," *Textile World*, Nov., 1961, p. 49.
[8] *Ibid.*, p. 50.

designed to find new end uses for textile products, and economic research which would aid the industry in planning its future production program. Some of the research could be conducted by existing Government agencies. But grants could also be made to universities and other research organizations capable of effectively assisting the textile industry. There is a need, for example, for sound projections of the future industrial and consumer demand for textile products; for a well-conceived and carefully executed program of market research, and for an expanded program of basic research to develop new industrial and consumer uses for fibers and fabrics.[9]

If this recommendation had been accepted by the United States Government and if the Government had followed the pattern set by its support of research in the domestic commercial fisheries industry, it would have meant that at the then annual rate of duties collected a research program for textile mill products would have had a fund of about $80 million a year. If four per cent, the national average, were used for basic research, about $3.2 million would have been provided annually.[10] In 1959, the calculated amount of duties collected on textile fabrics and apparel, excluding all fibers, was approximately $240 million.[11]

On May 2, 1961, President Kennedy issued a program of assistance to the United States textile industry. One of his directives called for an expanded research program by the Department of Commerce, covering new products, processes and markets in cooperation with union and management groups. The Department of Commerce forthwith expanded its research program and several useful economic studies were completed which dealt with the problems of the domestic textile producers. Research on new products and process is underway.[12] In addition to this action by the Commerce Department, the Department of Defense has been spending during the past several years over a million dollars a year on textile research.[13]

The Department of Agriculture likewise contributes to textile research by maintaining and operating laboratories such as the

[9] Report of the Committee on Interstate and Foreign Commerce, of United States Senate, 86 Cong., 1st Sess., Rept. No. 42, p. 27.
[10] Basic Research Related to New Uses for Textiles, U. S. Dept. of Comm., 1961, p. 48.
[11] U. S. Imports of Merchandise for Consumption and General Imports of Merchandise, U. S. Dept. of Comm., Bur. of Census, Table IM-145, 1958.
[12] Problems of the Textile Industry, Second Supp. Rep. of Com. of Commerce, U. S. Senate, 87th Cong., 2nd Sess., Rept. No. 1314.
[13] Current Needs in Research Relevant to the Interests of the United States Textile Industry, National Research Council, 1962, p. 4.

Southern Regional Research Laboratory in New Orleans. Among other things this laboratory has done considerable work on cotton utilization.

The National Bureau of Standards through its work has had an impact on testing and quality control throughout the textile industry.

The textile schools have been established primarily for teaching purposes but a number of them conduct research programs. The work of graduate students is noteworthy and has on numerous occasions resulted in real contributions to the textile industry. Good graduate programs have been developed at Textile Research Institute, Princeton, New Jersey, and the Institute of Textile Technology, Charlottesville, Virginia, where students are required to complete creditable research projects to qualify for advanced degrees. Both of these institutes also engage in research projects for textile companies.

Perhaps all textile colleges engage in some form or other of research and, generally speaking, their programs have been increased during the past fifteen or twenty years. This is particularly true of the Department of Textile Research at North Carolina State University, Raleigh, North Carolina, where much "mill-oriented" research is carried on. In doing this work the college has served the collective needs of the industry which the individual units of the industry could not provide by themselves. Thus industry has had its research needs filled in a centralized laboratory serving all mills at a cost they can afford.[14]

Relatively few of the textile mills presently have research programs. Some executives believe that research programs do not pay; others can't afford them. Some mills depend in part or entirely on unaffiliated research organizations to care for their needs. In numerous mills the research laboratory is largely in name only, while in many instances work is limited to determining those things that provide improvement in quality and manufacturing cost using existing machinery and processes. However, mention might be made of a goodly number of mills active in this area of endeavor. For instance Dan River Mills organized a formal research department in 1943; Springs Cotton Mills has diligently explored the field of fabric finishes; and for more than twenty-five years West Point Manufacturing Company Division of West Point Pepperell, Inc., has worked in the area of applied research and now holds a number of patents which relate mainly to process.

---

[14] Malcolm Campbell, "Present State of Textile Research," *Canadian Textile Journal,* Apr. 4, 1958, p. 67.

United Merchants and Manufacturers recently announced that it is expanding its research center in Langley, South Carolina, for a second time in three years. The laboratory and pilot plant space is being tripled. Other companies such as Stevens, Burlington, Deering-Milliken, and M. Lowenstein and Sons have greatly expanded their research programs during the past decade.

It would not be feasible to describe the organization and work of the research departments of all of the above-mentioned companies, but passing mention may be made of one of them. Burlington Industries, rated as the largest textile company in America, before World War II, had only small research facilities chiefly concerned with quality control. With the entry of man-made fibers, the management became aware that their competitive position depended on their ability to develop new products as well as the performance of products already being manufactured. Research and development therefore became an economic necessity.

The reasons given by Burlington for establishing its research and development program are as follows: (1) To keep abreast of rapid technological changes and to take advantage of new developments, including the vast sources of technical knowledge becoming available for research work all over the world. (2) To cope with the growing complexity of raw materials and products. (3) To search for simpler manufacturing processes in order to reduce costs. (4) To improve quality and production methods. (5) To attempt to solve some of the age-old textile problems that have confounded the industry. (6) To meet the demand for research in many new and complex areas occasioned by the growing diversification of the company. (7) To provide the leadership to which it is committed as a major corporation.

Burlington's research center, located in Greensboro, North Carolina, is staffed by some sixty research chemists, physicists and laboratory technicians who are concerned with basic and applied research. Its activities include five primary research areas: (1) Chemical laboratory where work is concerned with organic and analytical chemistry, with the study and application of finishing chemicals, sizing and yarn treatments. New chemicals are also explored to produce new or improved textile products. (2) Dyeing application laboratory is used in the development of new and more efficient techniques for dyeing materials and provides technical services to all company divisions in solving major problems relating to dyeing and finishing. (3) Polymer and elastomer laboratory experiments with the combination of elastomers or polymers and a wide range of materials to produce specialized fabrics for home and industrial use. (4) Electronic mechanical laboratory conducts research into the properties of fibers and their behavior under mechanical treatments to which they are subjected in processing; it also designs and develops electronic and electro-mechanical devices for testing and control. (5) Physical evaluation laboratory evaluates fibers, yarns, fabrics and garments and establishes both test methods and standards of performance.

Burlington Industries also has some twenty-five divisional laboratories located in various areas. These laboratories are used to evaluate raw materials and end products, explore new and modified production equipment, and apply theories of the Central Laboratory.

In corporate research and technical training Burlington is concerned with broad market research and economic trend analysis, long-range diversification studies, training for highly qualified technical personnel, application of data processing techniques and coordinating research projects conducted for the company by outside agencies.

The new fiber and fabric division is concerned with the evaluation, application and economics of all new and modified yarns and fibers and their use in the development of new fibers.

The new product development, located in New York, is concerned with new products and new processes which result in new products. It functions to bring together merchandising, manufacturing and research and serves as a contact with other companies on new products, processes and machinery.

To coordinate this program Burlington established a Technical Council which meets in Greensboro at least four times a year, at which times the technical heads of the manufacturing divisions are informed of the results of the work at Central Research. A Central Technical Information Service and library provides information to research and manufacturing personnel throughout the company.

The National Cotton Council of American and Cotton Producers Institute conducts and supports research on cotton. Extensive research on behalf of the textile industry presently is being done by the dyestuff manufacturers, the chemical companies, the electronic industry, textile machinery makers and manufacturers of auxiliary equipment.

Numerous new products have resulted from the research efforts of the textile and allied industries: stretch yarns for socks and sport coats, wash and wear fabrics achieved through blends, all cotton permanent press fabric for women's dresses, men's sport shirts, bedspreads and curtains, sheets and pillow cases, texturized yarns for knitwear, and other materials for apparel and house furnishings.

A number of research projects relating to cotton have been mentioned in various issues of *Cotton Research Notes,* issued periodically by the National Cotton Council of America. In 1963 the Cotton Producers Institute was reported to have supported the Harris Research Laboratories in studies to explore the potential of using heat and pressure, along with swelling agents, to set creases in cotton fabrics; to develop suitably styled and designed all-cotton men's suits having maximum wrinkle resistance, freedom from seam pucker, good shape and crease retention and good wash-wear properties; to explore development of winter-wear cotton fabrics which will retain wool-like warmth and appearance properties during wear and laundering. Also reported was support to Texas Woman's University to study comparative performance of 100 per cent modified rayons, cotton-modified rayon blends, and 100 per cent cottons.[15]

Among grants extended in 1963 by the Foundation for Cotton Research and Education was (1) to the Textile Research Institute to develop fundamental information leading to more effective wash-wear finishes for cotton; and (2) to the Harris Research Laboratories to find a practical method for improving the performance of cotton rugs and carpets by reducing flattening and matting.[16]

In 1964 the Cotton Producers Institute approved eleven new projects and renewed ten projects from the 1963 program. This research effort represented a direct producers' contribution of about $800,000. Counterpart funds brought the total to approximately $1.3 million. Included in these projects were grants (1) to the Southern Utilization Research and Development Division for studies directed toward engineering specific fabric constructions for use with new chemical finishes to expand markets and (2) to North Carolina State College for exploratory research on methods of selectively removing short fibers only from cotton during mill processing.[17]

In 1965 the Cotton Producers Institute approved seven new cotton research projects and renewed twenty projects. These twenty-seven studies represented a total contribution of about $867,000. Included among the new projects were grants (1) to Harris Research Laboratories to explore pilot plant resin treatment of cotton carpeting and its effect on serviceability; and (2) to

---

[15] *Cotton Research Notes,* Oct., 1963, pp. 2-4.
[16] *Ibid.,* p. 4.
[17] *Ibid.,* Jan., 1964, p. 2.

Gagleardi Research Laboratories to explore one-side resin treatment of fabric as a means of improving abrasion resistance of durably creased cotton.

The United States Department of Agriculture currently lends support in various areas of cotton utilization research. The program, administered by the Southern Utilization Research and Development Division, comprises grants and contracts distributed over thirteen states and the District of Columbia. Included, for example, were grants (1) to Southern Research Institute, Birmingham, Alabama, to study the development of wash-wear cotton fabric with improved moisture absorptivity by use of reacting swelling agents; (2) to Massachusetts Institute of Technology for investigation of the configurational interactions between fibers and yarns in the region of local deformations in woven cotton cloth; (3) to North Carolina State University to determine the effects of stretching and comprehensive shrinkage in combination with chemical treatments on ease-of-care properties of cotton fabrics; and (4) to Texas Woman's University to study the development of improved durable weather-resistant, water-repellant finishes for out-door cotton fabrics.[18]

Twenty-two projects in various areas of cotton utilization are currently active in ten foreign countries; France, India, Israel, The Netherlands, Poland, Spain, Sweden, Switzerland, United Kingdom and West Germany. These projects are financed by Public Law 480 funds which became available from sales of surplus United States agricultural commodities overseas. Some of the subjects for which grants were extended for study were (1) the relation between fine structure and mechanical properties of cotton fibers by swelling and stretching treatments; (2) the determination of effect of drafting forces in high-draft systems on uniformity and strength of cotton yarns; (3) the fundamental investigation of setting reactions for cotton fabrics and garments; and (4) the structural elements of cotton fiber in response to stress in deformation and recovery.[19]

The above-mentioned research projects are but a few of the hundreds of projects now being studied by private, governmental, educational and other organizations doing research in textiles. Their titles suggest the extent of their endeavors.

In a report made for the Department of Commerce the *ad hoc* Textile Research Committee stated that government support (or joint industry–Government support, if feasible) was desirable in

---

[18] *Ibid.*, April, 1965, p. 3.
[19] *Ibid.*, Sept.-Oct., 1964, p. 5.

several areas considered basic to the establishment of a sound foundation of knowledge to textile materials, textile manufacturing processes, and textile marketing. Examples of the study areas which the Committee felt warranted direct support included the following:[20] (1) Study of fiber structure and characterization of fiber properties which (a) determine their processability in *single* fiber systems and in *blends* and (b) and affect their performance in end products, particularly in blended fabrics. (2) Analysis and experimental evaluation of the contribution of textile structural geometry to product performance. (3) Fundamentals of textile (physical) manufacturing processes with emphasis on the interaction between fiber properties and process dynamics—the basic engineering of fiber manipulation. (4) Fundamentals of finishing, or wet processing, of textile materials (chemical engineering). (It is expected that such studies will establish a sound basis for development or selection of methods for drying, curing, heat setting, etc., of fibrous materials and structures.) (5) Analysis of the physical and chemical requirements of non-textile materials commonly used in consumer and industrial items with a view to highlighting the potential contributions of fibrous materials to such areas. (6) Study and analysis of the special requirements of materials and systems useful in space exploration with a view towards defining the potential of textile materials in such applications. (7) Study of advances in the textile sciences made in Iron Curtain countries. (8) Study of the biophysics of man's reaction to his physical environment. (What system best suits the basic comfort requirements of man?) (9) Study of the psychology of man's aesthetic reactions to textile fabrics and clothing. (What motivates consumer reactions?)

The Committee also recommended direct Government support to graduate education which emphasized research experience in textiles. These recommendations included: (1) support of graduate students and post-doctoral fellows studying in a range of scientific disciplines and applying their knowledge to textile problems; and (2) support of faculty positions in graduate schools providing a program of textile research.[21]

Government officials are aware of the value of research. Governor Dan K. Moore of North Carolina pointed out in his address to the Southern Textile Association that "Research in the textile is a must. It is the key to basic improvements in both productivity and quality; I am told by textile authorities that research in the

---

[20] *Current Needs in Research Relevant to the Interests of the United States Textile Industry,* National Academy of Sciences, National Research Council, 1962, pp. 16-17.
[21] *Ibid.,* p. 17.

carding operation has produced significant results in just the past two years. In 1963, only 10 to 12 pounds per hour was standard. Today, through research, the standard is 30 to 40 pounds per hour."[22]

More textile mill executives are expressing the need for research and few meetings of representatives pass without reference to that subject. Mr. Roger Millikin, President of Deering Milliken Corporation, stated that "Deering Milliken long ago had made a deep and total commitment to build its future on a foundation of research."[23]

Mr. William E. Reid, President of Riegel Textile Corporation, in his presidential speech to the American Textile Manufacturers Institute, devoted considerable time to this subject of research stating in part:

> The "Something New" gained remarkable impetus during the year. Treatment of fabrics to impart permanency of crease is the newest basic development to win broad consumer acceptance. Greater emphasis on stretch fabrics during 1964 widened the horizons for ever increasing uses for this type of cloth, at first, limited largely to ski pants and nurses uniforms. And more exciting blends of fibers brought more exciting fabrics to find their way into apparel for men and women, boys and girls, and also for home furnishings and industrial uses.

A somewhat similar reference to research was made by Mr. George Asnip in his presidential speech in 1964 to the South Carolina Textile Manufacturer's Association. He pointed out that cloth had been more or less a static product over the years but research in the past decade had changed that. "Today's product," he said, "can be made of a proliferation of fibers and possesses characteristics unthought of a few years ago. Today's yard of cloth can iron itself in the wash, or stretch, or provide great warmth even though it is almost featherweight. Some even glow in the dark."

Finally, an industry, which because of its multiple units and lack of funds delayed research, has become aware of changing times and conditions. Markets lost to foreign competitors and local producers of related products emphasized the need for action. Changes have been and will be made in the industry. The public is constantly being made aware of new and better products being introduced, and consequently new markets are available. Such progress doubtless led Mr. Fuller E. Callaway, President of Callaway Mills, to prophesy that "a substantial portion of our sales ten years from now will come from products that do not exist at present."

[22] *Textile Bulletin*, July, 1965, p. 35.
[23] *Ibid.*, p. 38.

CHAPTER X

THE RELATIVE POSITION OF THE UNITED STATES WITH OTHER COUNTRIES

To better understand the position of the textile industry of the United States it is doubtless beneficial to note conditions in other textile manufacturing countries. As Great Britain early led the world in the manufacture of cotton and was the forerunner of the industry in America, consideration might first be given its development in that nation.

The early industry centered around Manchester for coal was plentiful there for developing steam power and the climate so humid that it was ideal for cotton manufacturing.

By the end of the first decade of the 19th Century about 5,000,000 spindles were in operation in the United Kingdom of which over 10 per cent were mule spindles. By 1880 the cotton industry was fully developed and in 1885 over 41,298,000 spindles were in operation. The peak was reached in 1917 when the number had increased to 60,973,381, but by 1950 it had declined to 29,580,000. During the period from July, 1956, to July, 1957, almost one and one-half million spindles had become inactive and between January, 1956, and January, 1957, the number of looms declined by about 29,000.

And in the United Kingdom, as in America, mills closed. According to the Minister of State Board of Trade, fifteen closed in 1954, ninety in 1955, ninety-six in 1956, and sixty in 1957. In about a five-year period, 249 single unit weaving mills, 80 horizontal spinning and doubling mills, and 30 finishing units closed.

There were numerous contributing factors to those unfavorable conditions of the cotton manufacturing industry in England. During World War II many cotton mills were closed and the machinery stored. After the war it was necessary to clean the machinery and to recruit labor, as many former cotton mill workers had found employment in other industries. In the meantime American mills, not badly affected by the war, had developed new techniques and enjoyed the use of modern machines. However it was reported that during the first decade after the war approximately $300,000,000 had been spent to re-equip English mills.

Trade unions in some areas opposed the introduction of new machinery and time and motion studies were declared taboo by certain labor leaders. Where there was modernization of mills, shift working was promoted to reduce costs, but here again some trade union resistance appeared and difficulties arose in obtaining operatives for additional shifts.

Added to these and other difficulties, cheap cotton cloth was imported from Asiatic countries made by low paid workers. The government gave some protection in the home market against non-Commonwealth textiles by establishing a tariff of 17½ per cent against piece goods and 20 per cent against make up goods. It also imposed quotas on textiles originating in Japan and China and allowed small quotas for other Communist countries.

Under the Ottawa Agreements of 1932, however, provision was made for Commonwealth goods to be admitted duty free in the United Kingdom. It was supposed that cotton goods would flow freely throughout the Commonwealth. However, both India and Pakistan imposed duties on English cotton goods and import licenses became difficult to obtain. Therefore, exports of cotton goods from England to these two countries declined but at the same time the importation of the commodities into England from India and Pakistan greatly increased. By 1958, imports of cotton piece goods into Britain exceeded Britain's exports of these goods. Conditions were slightly improved by an understanding between England and India and Pakistan.

With the contraction of the market for English cottons came a reduction in profits, thus limiting capital replacement. To assist the industry Parliament in 1959 passed the Cotton Industry Act. The 12,800,000 mule and 10,450,000 ring spindles in 1956 had been reduced to 2,724,000 and 6,741,000, respectively, by 1961. During the same period the total number of looms was reduced from 311,000 to 164,000. However, a great deal of the capacity of the industry was already closed down when the scrapping program was instituted as provided by the Act of 1959. There was, therefore, only about an overall reduction of 22 percent in spinning and 10 percent in weaving machines.[1]

Two-thirds of the cost of scrapping the textile machinery or for closing down production units was to be paid by the Government and one-third by the textile firms remaining in operation. However, of the estimated total cost of the schemes, £25.7m, including payments to textile workers, the Government's contribution approached £11.5m.[2]

---

[1] A. McPhie, "The Changing Structure of the U. K. Cotton Industry," *The Textile Weekly*, May 28, 1965, pp. 955.
[2] *Ibid.*

During the period 1946 to 1957, about £165,000,000 was expended on capital projects in the textile industry, or an average annual investment of £13,700,000. By comparison the average capital investment in the United States between 1951 and 1956 was $420 million, or almost twelve times the United Kingdom figure.[3]

The Reorganization Schemes were therefore supplemented by a re-equipment scheme in which the Government offered grants of one-quarter of the cost of re-equipment and modernization completed before July, 1964. It is estimated that schemes valued at £60m were carried out.

Since the termination of the scrapping part of the Reorganization Schemes, over 100 mills closed without compensation to shareholders or workers. This was caused largely by the importation of cheaply produced goods into Britain.[4]

While the various schemes reduced total spindleage by about two-thirds between 1958 and 1964, single yarn production decreased only about 19 per cent over the same period. Likewise during the six year period the number of looms in place fell by 52 per cent, but the decrease in the overall output, measured in linear yards, was only 19 per cent.

During the period 1958 to 1964 the production of woven cloth decreased while the production of man-made fibers increased as may be noted in the following table:

TABLE XXII

PRODUCTION OF WOVEN FABRIC FOR YEARS 1958 AND 1964 AND
PERCENTAGE CHANGE[5]
(million linear yards)

	1958	1964	Change
Cotton	1,428	1,035	28%
Man-made fibers and mixtures of which:	601	609	1%
Tire cord fabric*			
Viscose	47	70	49%
Other	2	8	4%
Continuous Filament:			
Rayons	159	212	33%
Other	69	91	30%
Spun	198	122	38%
Filament/spun mixtures	40	37	7½%
Other mixtures	86	69	20%

* Figures are in million lbs. and are included in the totals on the basis of one yard per lb.

---

[3] Allan Ormerod, "The Prospects of the British Cotton Industry," *Textile Recorder,* Feb., 1963, p. 47.

[4] A. McPhie, "The Changing Structure of the U. K. Cotton Industry," *The Textile Weekly,* May 28, 1965, p. 956.

[5] A. McPhie, "The Changing Structure of the U. K. Cotton Industry," *The Textile Weekly,* May 28, 1965, pp. 998.

Shift working has also been increased with about 41 per cent of the spinning spindles running on two or three shifts compared with 5 per cent before the reorganization schemes. About 55 per cent of the yarn spun and about 60 per cent of the cloth woven in the industry is produced on machinery working two or three shifts.[6]

However, Allan Ormerod, writing in 1963, pointed out that there were still two million mule spindles in production and that a large portion of the ring spindles were of pre-war design and performance. He also contended that obsolete equipment had also been retained in other parts of the industry, particularly in the weaving and finishing sections where about 110,000 non-automatic looms were in production, or over two-thirds of the total weaving capacity.[7] He questioned the economy of running an obsolete type of equipment on multi-shift systems with shift premiums and shorter shift hours. To rid the industry of all non-automatic looms, mules, obsolete spinning, preparation, weaving and spinning plants, according to Mr. Ormerod's estimate, would cost over £400,000,000 and the operation could then be staffed by 75,000 fewer workers than presently used.[8] Thus it would seem that much more needs to be done in re-equipment of mills to bring the textile industry of Britain up to the best world standards.

Britain has had a real source of worry over importation of textiles. In 1964, 767 million square yards of cotton piece goods were imported, which was almost three-fourths as much as the United Kingdom produced. The total was even greater when make-up goods, whose value in 1964 was about £40 million, was added.

The cotton industry has strongly objected to the government's policy on the importation of textiles. Cotton manufacturers are quick to point out that theirs is the only major industry in the United Kingdom to face large scale, low cost competition from duty free imports from the Commonwealth. Quantities of material are also imported from developing nations. This finally resulted in the United Kingdom's annually taking between one-third and two-fifths of its domestic requirements of cotton goods in the form of imports while, the English contended, the United States and the European Economic Community took well below ten per cent.[9]

Since 1958 various inter-industry or inter-governmental arrangements have been consummated which limited the importation of cotton goods from certain low wage countries. Most sources were

---

[6] *Ibid.,* p. 956.
[7] *Textile Recorder,* Feb., 1963, p. 48.
[8] *Ibid.,* p. 51.
[9] A. McPhie, "The Changing Structure of the U. K. Cotton Industry," *The Textile Weekly,* May 28, 1965, p. 1000.

therefore controlled quantitatively, but supplies from other areas entered the market. Import licensing was instituted in May, 1964, and effective control was realized; but importers had placed contracts with the new suppliers, so imports continued to grow during the year. For this and other reasons, such as quota carry-over arrangements, imports of cotton-textiles in the United Kingdom reached a new high in 1964.

The Cotton Board of England has suggested that individual arrangements be replaced by a global quota, preferably on all imports but, failing this, on imports from all developing countries. If the quota is confined to developing countries, effective arrangements would have to be made to prevent low-cost goods entering the United Kingdom by way of Western countries.

Because of the excessively low price of the textile imports, many mills were forced to close during the present decade. The industry consequently feels that it should have adequate protection against low-wage imports and continuing protection against duty free imports from all Commonwealth countries in addition to quotas.

The Cotton Board recognizes the merits of the Long Term Arrangement but has proposed its revision. It has suggested that all developed countries take not less than ten per cent of its domestic requirements of cotton manufacturers from under-developed countries. Above the figure of ten per cent there would be a small growth factor ceasing at twenty-five per cent.[10]

The British proposal of a global import quota equal to the average volume of imports in 1962-1964 raised various questions. Since there would be no breakdown by country or product, it is suggested that a scramble would occur each year to get as much as possible into the United Kingdom from each country before the quota was filled. Developed nations like Japan would be excluded from the market. This would doubtless increase the pressure on the United States to take more textiles, whereas for some years America has been trying to persuade European nations to admit more textiles from Asia.

When approving the long-term agreement the United Kingdom did so on condition that the growth provision not apply to it since imports amounted to 40 per cent of domestic consumption. These imports, however, were concentrated in the Commonwealth countries.

Various obstacles must be overcome if the textile industry is to prosper in the United Kingdom. First there must be a change in

---

[10] *Ibid.*, p. 1053.

the attitudes of various members of labor unions who are reluctant to accept innovations brought about by modern machinery. Second, there must be a complete program for modernization including possibly the construction of new buildings so that modern machinery can be so placed as to assure greatest efficiency in operation. Third, there must be a well defined governmental policy to give confidence to the industry so that it will not only attract the necessary capital but also capable young men to develop the industry.

Japan

In August, 1910, Japan had 1,943,000 spindles which by 1920 had increased in number to 3,192,000. In 1937, just prior to World War II, the largest number, 8,973,000, of spindles was reached and Japan rivaled the nations of the world in the textile trade. During World War II the number was reduced and in 1945 only 336,000 spindles were in operation. However, with some assistance from the United States, in 1948 the number of spindles had increased to 2,229,000. They increased every year until 1957 when 8,430,000 were in place. Then there was a general decline to 6,003,000 operating spindles in 1962. In the same year there were 296,000 looms in operation in Japan.[11]

The textile industry of Japan is not, however, without its troubles. Imports to Asian and African markets decreased as well as to some other parts of the world. Communist China, Hong Kong, India, Pakistan, Taiwan and other developing countries are offering competition to Japan as an exporter of textiles.

One of the major problems facing Japan, as it does the United States and European countries, is a change in the world's trade structure of cotton products, caused by the development of cotton manufacture in newly rising countries. This question not only involves the old problem of shrinking markets in these countries due to raised self-sufficiency in cotton goods but also sharpened competition in world trade due to the advance of the industry in these countries.

The countries which formerly imported large quantities of cotton goods from Japan still require quality goods while exports by newly developing countries are mostly low in quality. Consequently, Japan is endeavoring to produce for export superior goods to adapt herself to the changing pattern of cotton goods trade in the world.

The total exports of cotton yarn from Japan declined from 39,143,000 kilograms in 1960 to 17,065,000 in 1962. Japan's Asia

---

[11] *Japan Cotton Statistics*, 1963, pp. 73-74.

market for yarn was cut approximately in half and the European market almost disappeared. However, some gains were made in North America and exports of yarn to South America enjoyed a four fold increase.[12]

In the three year period, 1960 to 1962, the export of cotton cloth from Japan increased from 1,191,153 to 1,211,060 square meters. Losses in markets in Asia, Europe and South America were more than balanced by increased exports of cotton cloth to Africa and North America.[13]

India

The number of cotton spinning spindles in India grew from 5,657,000 in 1910 to 9,731,000 in 1938 and, by 1961, they numbered 13,985,000.[14] In 1950, with 10.8 million spindles and about 200,000 power looms, India became the world's leading textile exporter, a position it lost to Japan the following year.

The cotton textile industry in India is the largest factory industry and employs the highest amount of capital and the largest number of persons. It is the biggest paymaster and its contribution to the national income is larger than any other industry in the country.[15]

In 1946 more than 50 per cent of the cotton textile factories were located in Bombay State but by a decade later there had been some spreading out. Presently, with slightly more than 40 per cent, Bombay State continues to enjoy the most predominant position in India in respect to the cotton textile industry.

The size of the plants varies from small mills employing less than one hundred operatives to those employing several thousand workers. For example, twenty-one Indian cotton mills employ less than twenty workers while twenty-eight mills have 5,000 or more employees. The most important size group is between 2,000 to 4,999 employees which enjoys the largest share in aggregate capital, employment and output.

The Indian cotton textile industry at times has been very profitable. During the war years, 1941-1945, the dividends of one firm ranged from ten to forty per cent. A study of twenty-eight mills in different parts of the country in 1956-1957 found that the dividends on ordinary shares ranged from six to thirty-two and one-half per cent.[16]

---

[12] *Ibid.*, p. 78.
[13] *Ibid.*
[14] *Ibid.*, p. 178.
[15] H. Chandra, "Indian Cotton Textile Industry," *Indian Textile Journal,* June, 1960, p. 478.
[16] *Ibid.*, p. 482.

During the past few years, however, Indian textiles have been losing ground in a number of their traditional markets, especially Sudan, British East Africa, Ethiopia, Aden, Burma and Malaya. In the meantime, Japan picked up some of these markets. The position of Japan vis-a-vis India is explained in a Supplement of *Texprocil Bulletin,* published by the Cotton Textile Export Promotion Council, as follows:

> In the case of both India and Japan the Asian markets constitute 40 per cent of the major consumers of their respective textiles. Of the remaining markets, Indian cotton piecegoods are routed in a large measure to the African markets, while Japanese cotton piecegoods are routed more or less uniformly to the African, European and American markets. Among the Oceanic markets both Australia and New Zealand appear as major consumers of Indian as well as Japanese piecegoods.

The decline in export of Indian cotton piece goods was greatest to African countries, dropping from 298.20 million yards in 1959 to 182.96 million yards in 1960. There was a rise of 32 million yards in exports to the United Kingdom while shipments to American and Oceanic zones remained about the same.

To find markets for cotton goods India sent a delegation to North and West Africa in 1961, and it reported the need of a vigorous drive to promote export trade. There had been a drop from 815.16 million yards in 1959 to 537.84 million yards in 1962 in export of cotton piece goods from India. This general decline led Neville Wadia, Chairman of the Cotton Textiles Export Promotion Council, to state:[17]

> I regret to say that, looking at the developments which are taking place in other countries, we are lagging miles behind. When compared to our competitors abroad, it can truly be said that our industry is tied hand and foot with curbs on production and expansion, resistance to rationalization and modern machinery, and numerous impositions of excise duties on finished products, as well as on a large number of items used in the course of manufacture. The industry on the one hand, and voluntary price control, on the other, has brought progress to a standstill. The industry cannot earn money with which to renovate to meet the ever increasing demand at home or abroad. It is indeed said that a country blessed with its own supply of raw cotton should be outstripped by the industries in

---

[17] M. P. Gandhi, "The Indian Situation," *Egyptian Cotton Gazette,* pp. 27-28.

countries not so fortunately placed. It is due to the fact that they are unfettered that they have been able to achieve such remarkable results.

During the past decade the Government of India permitted the installation of automatic looms and by 1960 out of a total of 205,000 looms 17,000 were automatic.[18] India faces the challenge of more modernization to save her textile industry and retain its competitive position in the foreign markets. In the modernization of the industry due regard will doubtless be given to the structural aspects in order that the units are of appropriate size so as to work efficiently and yield maximum productivity and profitability.

West Germany

In 1955 there were 6,006,000 spindles in West Germany, but by 1960 the number had declined to 5,909,000.[19] There were also in 1960 116,400 looms in that country of which 47,400 were automatic.[20] Production of cotton cloth in West Germany declined from 1,673.84 million in 1960 to 1,573.56 million square yards in 1961. Between 1960 and 1962 exports of cotton yarn declined from 6.36 to 5.24 millions of pounds, while during the same period exports of cotton piece goods declined from 284.80 thousand to 248.52 thousand quintals.

West Germany is experiencing rough competitive conditions and 140 small firms closed down in 1965. Modernization of the industry, expanded some 30 per cent over 1963, amounted to $121 million in 1964. Production per worker increased by about 56 per cent between 1958 and 1964 but the three-shift operation is virtually unknown.[21]

Several plans for retiring less efficient spinning capacity which involve per-spindle compensation from a Government-industry pool have been discussed. The adoption of such a plan would doubtless result in the establishment of larger economic units to meet future competitive conditions.

United States and Other Countries

Some idea of the relative position of the textile industry of the United States as compared with other countries of the world may be obtained from the following table.

[18] International Cotton Advisory Committee.
[19] *Japan Cotton Statistics, 1963*, p. 178.
[20] International Cotton Advisory Committee.
[21] *Daily News Record*, Sept. 27, 1965, p. 14.

101

TABLE XXIII

COTTON SPINNING SPINDLES IN PLACE FOR SPECIFIED
COUNTRIES AND YEARS

Country	1939 (January)	1950 (January) 1000 spindles	1960 (December)
United States	25,911	23,286	19,916
China	4730	4251	9600
U.S.S.R.	10,350	9483	10,800
India	10,054	10,534	13,864
Japan	11,502	3739	13,218
West Germany	12,225	5785	5909
France	9794	8148	5802
Brazil	2765	3284	3840
United Kingdom	36,322	29,580	9710
Pakistan	0	169	1941
Italy	5324	5566	4611
Poland	1764	1067	2001
Spain	2000	2210	2589
Egypt (U.A.R.)	251	499	1185
Argentina	329	512	1038
Mexico	884	986	1350
Turkey	104	276	793
East Germany	0	750	1150
Czechoslovakia	3330	2331	1950
Belgium	1984	1802	1493
Netherlands	1241	1170	1020
Canada	1159	1117	817
Hong Kong	0	0	490
Portugal	444	536	1101
Others	5181	6268	10,049
World total	142,467	117,081	116,188

Source: International Cotton Advisory Committee.

It may be noted that in 1939 the United States ranked next to the United Kingdom in total number of spindles, 25,911,000 as compared with 36,322,000 spindles. By 1960 both of these countries had reduced their number of spindles, the United States to 19,916,000 and the United Kingdom to 9,710,000, the latter being done under a program described earlier in this chapter. Thus the United States leads the nations in number of spindles. Other countries that reduced their spindleage between 1939 and 1960 were West Germany from 12,225,000 to 5,909,000, France 9,794,000 to 5,802,000, Italy 5,324,000 to 4,611,000, Belgium 1,984,000 to 1,493,000, Netherlands 1,241,000 to 1,020,000 and Canada 1,157,000 to 817,000.

Increases in the number of spindles between 1939 and 1960 were enjoyed in a number of countries including China 4,730,000 to

9,600,000, India 10,054,600 to 13,864,000, Japan 11,502,000 to 13,218,000, Spain 2,000,000 to 2,589,000, Egypt 251,000 to 1,185,000, Argentina 329,000 to 1,038,000, and Portugal 444,000 to 1,101,000. Pakistan had no cotton spinning spindles in 1939 but had 169,000 in 1950. This number had increased to 1,941,000 by 1960. While Hong Kong had none in 1950, in 1960 they numbered 490,000.

It may be noted that the reduction in the number of spindles occurred in the countries where higher wages prevail and the increase was in low-wage areas. On "Others," which includes some small and so-called "developing nations," the number of spindles jumped from 5,181,000 in 1939 to 10,049,000 in 1960.

The number of looms affords another yardstick with which to measure the industry. This is illustrated in the following table which shows the number of automatic and ordinary cotton looms by countries in 1960.

TABLE XXIV

AUTOMATIC AND ORDINARY COTTON LOOMS, BY COUNTRIES, DECEMBER 31, 1960

Country	Automatic	1960 Ordinary 1000 looms	Total
Japan	52.8	319.7	372.5
United States	320.3	0	320.3
U.S.S.R.	98.0	128.0	226.0
India	17.0	188.6	205.6
United Kingdom	46.0	122.0	168.0
China	36.0	116.0	152.0
Brazil	24.7	78.1	102.8
West Germany	69.0	47.4	116.4
France	66.3	49.9	116.2
Italy	77.2	20.8	98.0
Spain	10.1	56.4	66.5
Poland	6.0	35.5	41.5
Mexico	10.0	30.0	40.0
East Germany	10.0	29.0	39.0
Czechoslovakia	16.4	21.0	37.4
Netherlands	16.4	16.4	32.8
Portugal	7.4	25.0	32.4
Belgium	11.1	19.7	30.8
Pakistan	18.0	12.0	30.0
Egypt (U.A.R.)	11.6	10.1	21.7
Argentina	14.8	5.4	20.2
Korea	3.8	14.0	17.8
Hong Kong	12.0	5.0	17.0
Rumania	2.6	14.0	16.6
Turkey	12.2	3.6	15.8

Country	Automatic	1960 Ordinary 1000 looms	Total
Yugoslavia	7.6	8.0	15.6
Canada	12.9	0.0	12.9
Other	107.7	79.8	187.5
World total	1097.9	1455.4	2553.3

Source: International Cotton Advisory Committee.

Japan with 372,500 leads the nations of the world in number of looms, but only 52,800 are automatic. While the United States is in second place in number, all 320,300 looms are automatic—an advantage which no other nation enjoys. Of the world total 2,553,300 in 1960, less than half, 1,097,900, of the looms were automatic and of that number approximately 30 per cent were located in the United States.

Having compared the number of spindles and the types and number of looms, note will be made of production of cotton yarn and cotton cloth in nations of the world.

TABLE XXV

PRODUCTION OF COTTON YARN IN THE SPECIFIED COUNTRIES
IN 1938 AND SINCE 1956

(In Millions of Pounds)

Country	1938	1956	1957	1958	1959	1960	1961	1962
Argentina	53.72	223.20	213.16	218.32	192.36	210.84	192.56	N.A.
Australia	(a)11.60	41.00	44.16	43.07	44.00	48.60	37.72	N.A.
Austria	68.36	52.60	56.92	58.40	55.68	58.76	62.56	59.52
Belgium	165.52	239.36	245.68	190.16	214.96	227.52	228.00	N.A.
Burma	(b)3.60	3.28	3.72	5.16	7.88	8.36	8.48	N.A.
Canada	119.24	147.28	140.88	132.28	137.12	131.92	145.40	155.28
Ceylon	1.24	1.64	1.92	1.84	1.80	2.16	N.A.	N.A.
Denmark(c)	16.96	15.32	18.36	16.03	18.45	17.24	16.80	17.48
U.A.R.	44.80	165.40	177.56	193.24	204.28	227.92	244.72	N.A.
Formosa	----	53.88	61.52	60.60	67.72	89.04	107.60	N.A.
France	504.00	521.00	584.16	593.44	539.20	619.64	616.60	572.16
Finland	27.52	33.12	36.52	31.04	38.36	40.36	36.92	35.80
Germany West(d)	(e)703.60	630.52	678.92	648.15	651.80	697.84	679.44	(l)831.00
Hong Kong	----	99.44	106.36	116.87	136.16	173.00	214.28	N.A.
India(f)	1,287.52	1,671.20	1,780.08	1,685.38	1,722.80	1,737.12	1,901.00	1,888.00
Italy	305.52	342.60	386.88	362.59	392.40	436.80	435.68	439.68
Korea So.	(g)59.56	67.60	90.92	96.45	106.88	108.36	94.52	N.A.
Mexico	(h)98.40	100.00	110.00	111.95	113.60	110.80	111.20	N.A.
Netherlands	(i)113.88	157.88	162.68	151.72	155.80	168.04	168.08	N.A.
Norway	6.00	5.84	5.56	5.25	5.96	6.08	6.52	7.08
Pakistan	----	300.40	316.92	345.12	386.84	411.00	412.60	N.A.
Philippines	N.A.	1.80	1.88	1.68	2.24	1.72	N.A.	N.A.
Portugal	45.88	79.40	77.92	81.88	84.96	113.44	124.36	N.A.
Salvador	N.A.	1.12	1.76	2.08	2.68	4.48	5.28	N.A.

Country	1938	1956	1957	1958	1959	1960	1961	1962
Spain	N.A.	122.16	134.88	167.56	158.56	176.84	195.84	188.24
Sweden(c)	60.72	59.84	62.24	59.16	55.88	56.04	55.64	N.A.
Switzerland	51.60	63.92	74.48	70.64	61.88	72.72	77.64	N.A.
Turkey(j)	15.76	58.36	59.96	60.28	60.64	60.76	72.24	N.A.
United Kingdom	1,052.00	702.32	727.24	631.24	606.20	596.16	554.24	492.76
U.S.A.(k)	2,456.00	3,724.00	3,808.00	3,628.00	4,068.00	3,936.00	3,880.00	3,960.00
Venezuela	----	12.80	14.36	13.92	19.04	17.28	18.92	N.A.
Yugoslavia(l)	N.A.	85.64	93.84	99.64	103.52	111.48	121.92	151.20

Remarks: (a) Twelve months ending June 30 of years stated. (b) Twelve months ending March 31 of years stated. (c) Figures from 1959 are not entirely comparable with previous years due to changes in classification. (d) Includes cotton waste yarn and other mixture yarns for 1938, and for 1956 onwards, cotton and cotton waste yarn only. (e) All Germany. (f) Including Pakistan in 1938 and Pondicherry in 1938 and from 1956. (g) All Korea. (h) Estimated from raw cotton used. (i) All yarns spun by the cotton and linen industry. (j) Government production only. (k) Figures (apart from 1958 and 1959) are estimated from raw cotton used. (l) Includes spun man-made fibre. N.A.–Not available.

Source: "Quarterly Statistical Review," The Cotton Board (U. K.) Arranged by The Cotton Economics Research Institute.

The production of cotton yarn in the United States increased from 3,808 million in 1957 to 3,880 million pounds in 1961. Other large producers of cotton yarn and the amount they produced in 1961 were India, 1,901; West Germany, 679.44; France, 616.60 and the United Kingdom, 554.24 millions of pounds.

TABLE XXVI

PRODUCTION OF COTTON CLOTH IN THE SPECIFIED COUNTRIES
IN 1938 AND SINCE 1957

Country	Unit	1938	1957	1958	1959	1960	1961	1962
Austria	Thousand	120.00	168.40	175.56	166.64	182.96	196.80	187.92
Belgium	Quintals	494.88	845.92	671.65	746.88	844.48	815.52	N.A.
Denmark(a)		47.20	61.48	56.60	62.44	62.56	N.A.	N.A.
Finland(b)		87.20	140.40	103.60	122.80	134.80	125.60	132.40
France		(j)1,780.00	1,907.96	1,966.75	1,903.68	2,112.88 (i)1,988.96 (i)1,983.36		
Italy		936.52	1,166.32	1,144.49	1,203.68	1,335.64	1,311.96	1,368.09
Mexico		377.40	456.68	444.33	492.08	487.96	448.44	N.A.
Netherlands(c)		(k)570.00	660.00	605.70	632.80	712.40	703.60	N.A.
Norway(d)		31.04	52.80	44.63	47.84	48.88	49.32	47.32
Portugal		162.32	258.44	278.26	283.20	343.64	N.A.	N.A.
Spain		N.A.	483.20	537.20	540.80	577.20	639.20	634.92
Sweden(a)		198.72	242.28	235.48	225.88	226.08	227.92	N.A.
Switzerland(c)		18.00	272.00	256.00	192.00	216.00	N.A.	N.A.
Canada	Million	213.48	283.08	267.80	262.92	262.36	302.36	N.A.
Formosa	Yards	----	170.00	160.08	170.72	192.68	204.00	N.A.
India(e)		4,305.12	5,317.40	4,926.96	4,925.44	5,048.36	5,141.56	4,989.00
Pakistan		N.A.	527.04	577.23	600.08	641.40	599.00	N.A.
Philippines		N.A.	15.36	11.33	10.60	5.84	N.A.	N.A.
Salvador(f)		N.A.	17.28	15.82	17.00	27.36	30.20	N.A.
Turkey(g)		39.80	171.88	170.95	172.12	173.08	164.48	N.A.
U. A. R.(h)		71.20	284.80	321.20	323.20	340.40	346.44	N.A.
United Kingdom		N.A.	1,627.60	1,428.60	1,336.80	1,293.56	1,234.72	1,047.36
U. S. A. (i)		N.A.	9,533.76	8,973.72	9,598.80	9,328.28	9,156.08	N.A.
Australia	Million	(l)(m)5.24	47.56	45.28	43.12	52.64	48.80	58.91
Germany (West)	Sq.Yards	2,220.00	1,632.20	1,550.28	1,550.28	1,673.84	1,573.56	N.A.
Korea (South)		(n)150.00	198.40	208.00	236.00	228.00	200.00	N.A.
Yugoslavia (d)		N.A.	247.76	261.85	273.72	305.76	321.96	361.98

Source: "Quarterly Statistical Review," The Cotton Board (U. K.) Arranged by The Cotton Economics Research Institute

105

The amount of cotton cloth produced by the United States declined from 9,533.76 million yards in 1957 to 9,156.08 million yards in 1961. During the same period production also declined in India from 5,317.40 to 5,141.56, and in the United Kingdom from 1,627.60 to 1,234.72 million yards.

France, Italy, Netherlands, Spain, Portugal, Pakistan and Yugoslavia were among those countries that enjoyed increased production during the period 1957 to 1961.

It would seem that the problems that disturb the textile industry in the United States are not confined to this area but have also been troublesome in other nations. The greatest change has taken place in the United Kingdom where the industry has been greatly reduced in size. As the industry grows in the underdeveloped countries, a further decline in the more developed nations may be expected.

CHAPTER XI

SUMMARY AND CONCLUSIONS

Beginning in 1643 ideas were advanced in America for the manufacture of cotton. The movement was stifled, however, because of restrictive legislation passed by the Parliament in England which prohibited the export of machinery for the manufacture of cotton. Finally Samuel Slater was able to overcome this difficulty and in 1791 a real beginning of cotton manufacture was launched in America. From this modest beginning, a mill with only 72 spindles driven by water, the industry expanded through New England and into the South. By 1840 the number of spindles in operation had increased to 2,248,631. Most of this development took place in the North for there were only 73 small cotton mills in operation in the Carolinas, Georgia and Alabama in 1840, and it was not until 1846 that the first large mill was established in the South. This was pioneered by William Gregg and was constructed at Graniteville, South Carolina.

Rapid expansion of the industry was enjoyed in both the North and the South during the last part of the nineteenth and the beginning of the twentieth century. In 1924 the all time high of 35,849,000 spindles were in operation in America. The following year, 1925, the South surpassed New England in number of spindles in operation and since then the movement of the industry has been to the cotton producing states.

Cotton manufacturers during the early period sought mill sites near water power. Thus many mills were built in sparsely settled places and recruited employees from small farms and villages over a large area. It was necessary, therefore, for the mills to build homes for this labor force, and, consequently, cotton mill villages sprang up in New England and, later, in the South with the spread of the industry. Facilities were added and through the years many mills made substantial investments to develop the religious, educational, recreational and cultural lives of the residents of their communities. With the development of modern means of transportation the need for mill villages declined, and within the past three or four decades the vast majority of mill homes have been sold. This, in general, has been considered advantageous to both employees and employers. The change-over in cities or towns was rather simple. In the smaller areas, however, mills often continued to care for such things as

107

water supply, collection of garbage, and fire protection. Some mills continue their recreational programs and have even enlarged them following sale of the villages.

In March, 1791, the Congress of the United States placed the first tax on cotton goods imported into this country. During the more than a century following, additional laws were enacted which provided for various changes in the tariff rates on textiles. At first competition with European countries was cause for alarm, but within recent decades Asiatic countries with cheap labor forces have troubled American producers. To care for trade difficulties the Cotton Textile Committee of the General Agreement on Tariffs and Trade negotiated in Geneva, Switzerland, a Long-Term Cotton Textile Arrangement on February 9, 1962. This agreement became effective October 1, 1962, and was to remain in force for five years. Among other things this Agreement provides for protection from market disruption of the contracting countries.

While no agreement is ever completely satisfactory, this one has brought relief to American cotton manufacturers and has been a positive advantage to various foreign countries. It is at present being reviewed for renewal with possible amendments.

American textile manufacturers have taken a dim view of the great increase of imports of textiles into this country from 1955 to 1960. Some mill executives contend that this increase was brought about in good measure by the encouragement of the American government through financial assistance for construction of mills abroad and as a result of tariffs inadequate to protect against low wage levels and low cotton costs of the exporting countries.

It is not probable that tariff changes will care for the problems, for our trade agreements and treaties are based on a most-favored-nation policy in which like imports are dutiable at the same rate, regardless of country of origin. Recourse, however, can be had by quantitative restrictions on imports and by international understandings to establish quotas in the categories of textiles in which the American Market is disturbed.

Wages in the textile industry, as in other industries, seem to have been very low during the nineteenth century. In the present century, however, there has been marked improvement, especially since World War II. The average hourly wage for textile mill products' employees was $1.36 in 1953, and by 1964 it had increased to $1.78. This compares well with the $1.79 an hour average paid apparel industry employees in 1964, and is substantially above the minimum wage of $1.25 established by federal law. The all manufacturing industries average hourly wage for 1964 was $2.53. The gap between textile wages and average hourly earnings of all manufacturing workers widened during the past decade.

The wage earners in the cotton goods industry continued to increase until 1942, when there was a total of 505,900. By 1960 this number had declined to 277,138. However, within recent years a more general designation, textile mill products industry, was created. In 1950 there were 1,256,000 employees in this industry, but the number had declined to 923,000 in 1965. The drop in textile employment is attributed to cyclical and long-term forces as well as to automation.

The production of rayon in the United States began during the early part of this century and by 1927 the cotton textile industry had developed a section that was weaving rayon on cotton machinery. This was followed in 1939 with the production of nylon. The first nylon hosiery for women was placed on sale in 1940 and by 1950 over 97 per cent of the women were wearing nylon stockings. Today it is an important ingredient of many products including paint brushes, ropes and automobile tires.

Other fibers presently produced in the United States include Acrylic, Terylene, Spandex, Olefin, Saran, Vinyon and Vinal. These and other man-made fibers have been well received by the public and thus given impetus to the expansion of the industry. In 1940 American mills produced 475.8 million pounds of man-made fibers but in 1963 production had increased to 2,691 million pounds. During the same period the per capita consumption of man-made fibers more than tripled in amount.

Within recent years a multitude of blends of man-made and natural fibers have been developed. New and improved products constantly appear on the markets to attract the consuming public. These are the direct result of the large expenditures by the man-made fiber companies on research. Continued intensive resarch will doubtless result in the constant growth of the industry.

Since World War I there has been a decrease in the number and an increase in the size of cotton mills. This movement slowed during the depression but between January, 1944 and July, 1946 at least 145 cotton mill mergers and acquisitions took place. Particularly active in the purchase of mills have been Burlington Industries, M. Lowenstein and Sons, and J. P. Stevens Company.

The merging of strong establishments like West Point-Pepperell, Dan River and Iselin Jefferson interests and the purchase of Morgan Jones Company by Springs Cotton Mills have doubtless further increased the financial strength of the companies. At the same time, some textile companies are diversifying while others are owned by related industries.

While it is generally felt that the mergers and acquisitions have not essentially altered the overall competitive structure of the textile industry, the advantages of integration are such as to encourage continuation of the movement.

The various textile machinery manufacturing companies are rapidly, through their research and developing departments, introducing new equipment to textile manufacturers. Notable advances have been made in all areas of the manufacturing process. The technological changes that increased the speed of the machines naturally led to increased production; yet, because of numerous labor-saving devices, fewer operatives are needed. In fact, the development of new machinery has been so rapid during recent years that machinery bought a few years ago is obsolete now.

The industry has remodeled and has also constructed many new mill buildings. In 1958 it spent $288,000,000 on new plants and equipment. This stepped up to $530,000,000 in 1960, increased to $760,000,000 in 1964, and it is estimated that the sum spent in 1965 amounted to over one billion dollars.

The United States lagged behind European countries in introducing textile education and design schools were the first institutions to be established, in the 1870's. The first textile school giving real instruction in textile work was established in Philadelphia in 1884, followed by the establishment of several training schools in New England.

During this century an imposing number of schools are devoting considerable attention to textiles. They include Massachusetts Institute of Technology, A. French Textile School of the Georgia Institute of Technology, Clemson University, School of Textiles of North Carolina State University at Raleigh, School of Textile Technology at Auburn University, Textile Research Institute, Princeton, New Jersey, Institute of Textile Technology, Charlottesville, Virginia, Lowell Technological Institute and Texas Technological College in Lubbock, Texas.

Graduates from these schools have been meeting the demands of industry for well trained men. The textile industry, in return, has made contributions to all the schools, both in money and equipment. The assistance of the J. E. Sirrine Textile Foundation to Clemson is noteworthy, while the North Carolina Textile Foundation has contributed over $2,000,000 to the School of Textiles of North Carolina State University.

110

All of the textile schools offer scholarships in various amounts to worthy students. Some of these scholarships are financed by grants to the schools from textile companies, while numerous scholarships are given directly to able students by mill executives.

To meet the demand of industries for skilled labor, vocational education courses were introduced into high schools. Later broader vocational educational programs were developed. Within this decade technical education centers established in South Carolina, industrial education centers in North Carolina, and similar centers in other states have been instrumental in training needed personnel for textile as well as for other industries.

The textile industry was late in establishing research departments. By 1940 some 13 companies were engaged in research in cotton and cotton products, and by 1946 the number had more than doubled. But the industry was still far behind most other industries in size and scope of its research effort in 1959.

In 1961 President Kennedy issued a program of assistance to the United States textile industry and called upon the Department of Commerce to expand its research program in this general area. Assistance to the industry is being contributed by other governmental agencies such as the Department of Agriculture and the National Bureau of Standards. The facilities of textile schools are used to advantage, and within recent years numerous companies have either established or expanded research centers. Various institutes are most helpful, but textile companies (e.g., Burlington Industries and Deering-Milliken) have appropriated in recent years large sums of money for research and development. But these efforts are too few in number. More of the industry will have to join in increased research efforts to find new end-uses and new industrial applications for textile mill products if it is to retain a healthy place in the industrial world.

Conditions in other textile manufacturing countries are not greatly unlike those in the United States. The United Kingdom, with over 60 million spindles in 1917, was the greatest textile producing country in the world. During recent decades, however, the number of spindles declined, and by 1960 they had been reduced to 9,710,000—and, as in America, numerous mills had closed.

A number of factors contributed to the difficulties experienced by the textile industry in England. The country came out of World War II in a very serious economic condition and the textile industry was badly crippled. The machinery, much of which had been stored during the war, needed to be reconditioned and labor had to be

111

recruited. In the meantime, American mills had developed new techniques and had added modern machinery to their mills.

There was trade union resistance in some parts of the United Kingdom to the introduction of shift working and time-and-motion studies.

The Ottawa Agreements of 1932 provided that Commonwealth goods be admitted duty free in the United Kingdom. An understanding between England and India and Pakistan concerning importation of cotton goods relieved the situation slightly. England lost markets both at home and abroad to these two low-wage Commonwealth countries.

A program for scrapping the textile industry was adopted at a total cost estimated at 27 million pounds. This was supplemented by a re-equipment scheme in which the government offered grants of one-quarter of the cost of re-equipment and modernization. A considerable quantity of out-of-date machinery, however, is still in use in England. A complete program of modernization is necessary if the textile industry of that country is to prosper.

Japan became a serious competitor in the textile market in the 1920's, and by 1937 there were 8,973,000 spindles operating in that country. Since World War II the number of spindles increased every year until 1958 when 8,430,000 were in place.

Within the present decade inroads have been made into Japan's foreign trade by Communist China, Hong Kong, India, Pakistan and Taiwan. This has forced Japan to curtail production, and in 1962 two million fewer spindles were operating in that country than in 1957.

The decline in India's foreign trade has caused that country to look toward modernization of the textile mills. This has been accomplished only in part. Much more needs to be done if India is to retain its position in the foreign markets.

West Germany is also suffering from competitive conditions in the textile industry. Modernization of the mills has expanded during recent years and several plans have been discussed for retiring less efficient spinning capacity.

Today the United States, with over 19 million spindles, leads all nations, but the number represents a decline of about six million since 1939. Generally speaking, the number of spindles in operation has declined in the high wage countries, while the spindles in the low wage, developing countries have increased in number.

With more of the developing countries engaging in, and other low wage countries increasing the manufacture of textiles, the world

112

market has been disturbed. This has affected adversely American export trade in textiles. Government action, therefore, is essential to protect the home market if the industry is to survive. At the same time, industry may well continue its ambitious program of modernization to reduce the cost of production and increase research facilities so that new and better textile products will be available on both domestic and foreign markets.

SELECTED BIBLIOGRAPHY

Official Documents

Hinrichs, A. F. *Wages in Cotton-Goods Manufacturing.* U. S. Bureau of Labor Statistics Bull. No. 663 (Washington: Government Printing Office).

Report of the Federal Commission on Merger Movement. Washington; Government Printing Office, 1948.

U. S. Congress, Senate, *Hearings before a Subcommittee on Interstate and Foreign Commerce,* 87th Cong., 1st Sess., February, 1961.

U. S., Congress, Senate, *Study of the Domestic Textile Industry. Hearings before a Subcommittee of the Committee on Commerce of U.S.,* 87th Cong., 2nd Sess., Jan., 1962.

U. S., Congress, Senate, *Problems of the Domestic Textile Industry, Hearings before a Subcommittee on Commerce,* 88th Cong. 1st Sess., May, 1963.

U. S., Department of Agriculture. *The American Textile Industry.* Agr. Econ. Rept. No. 58. (Washington: Government Printing Office, Nov., 1964.)

U. S., Department of Agriculture. *Changes in the American Textile Industry.* Tech. Bull. 1210. (Washington: Government Printing Office, 1959.)

U. S., Department of Agriculture. *The Demand for Textile Fibers in the United States.* Tech. Bull. No. 1301. (Washington: Government Printing Office, November, 1963.)

U. S., Department of Commerce. *Basic Research Related to New Uses for Textiles.* (Washington: Government Printing Office, 1961.)

U. S., Department of Commerce. *Cycles and Trends in Textiles.* (Washington: Government Printing Office, 1958.)

U. S., Department of Commerce. *Patterns and Problems of Technical Innovation in American Industry: Report to National Science Foundation.* (Washington: Office of Technical Services, U. S. Dept. of Commerce, 1963.)

U. S., Department of Commerce. *Textile Outlook for the Sixties.* (Washington: Government Printing Office, 1960.)

U. S., Department of Labor. *History of Wages in the United States from Colonial Times to 1929.* Bureau of Labor Statistics Bulletin No. 663. (Washington: Government Printing Office.)

U. S., Department of Labor. *Industry Wage Survey, Cotton Textiles, May, 1963.* Bureau of Labor Statistics Bulletin No. 1410. (Washington: Government Printing Office.)

U. S., Department of Labor. *Trade and Technical Education in the United States.* Bureau of Labor Statistics Bulletin No. 54 (1904), pp. 1369-1417.

Books and Periodicals

Andrews, John B. "The New Industrial South," *American Legislative Review,* Vol. 38, No. 1 (March, 1928).

Andrews, Mildred B. *Profit Life of Textile Machinery.* Vienna, Va.: American Textile Machinery Assoc., 1958.

Backman, J., and M. R. Gainsbrugh. *The Economics of the Cotton Textile Industry.* New York: The Conference Board, 1946.

Bader, Louis. *World Developments in the Cotton Industry.* New York: New York University Press, 1925.

Bagnall, W. R. *The Textile Industry of the United States.* Vols. II-VI. Cambridge, Mass.: Riverside Press, 1893.

Burgy, J. H. *The New England Cotton Textile Industry.* Baltimore: The Waverly Press, 1932.

Cameron, E. H. *Samuel Slater.* Portland, Maine: Fred L. Tower Co., 1960.

Campbell, Malcolm. "Present State of Research," *Canadian Textile Journal* (April, 1958), pp. 65-68.

Chandra, H. "Indian Cotton Textile Industry," *Indian Textile Journal* (June, 1960), pp. 478-484.

Clark, V. S. *History of Manufactures in the United States.* Vol. III. New York: Peter Smith, 1949.

Copeland, M. T. *The Cotton Manufacturing Industry of the United States.* Cambridge, Mass.: Harvard University Press, 1912.

_____ "Duties on Cotton Goods in Tariff Act of 1910," *Quarterly Journal of Economics,* Vol. 24 (April, 1910), pp. 422-428.

Davis, Charles S. *The Cotton Kingdom in Alabama.* Montgomery: Alabama State Department of Archives and History, 1939.

Delaney, W. "Education and Research in the Textile Industry," *Textile Age,* Vol. 12 (January, 1948), p. 9.

_____ "Looking at the Future of Cotton Textiles," *Textile Bulletin,* Vol. 69 (November 1, 1945), pp. 20, 22, 26.

_____ "Plans in Progress in Textile Research," *Textile Colorist and Converter,* Vol. 68 (Jan., 1946), pp. 14-15.

_____ "Research in the Textile Industry," *Textile Recorder,* Vol. 61 (July, 1944), pp. 71-73.

115

_____ "Textile Research Gains Stature," *American Wool Cotton Reporter,* Vol. 61 (Oct. 16, 1947), pp. 17-18.

Dodd, W. E. *The Cotton Kingdom.* New Haven: Yale University Press, 1919.

The Economic Almanac. Published by the National Industrial Conference Board in cooperation with *Newsweek,* 1964.

Gandhi, M. P. "The Indian Textile Situation," *Egyptian Cotton Gazette* (Jan. Feb., 1963), pp. 25-29.

Goldsmith, P. H. *The Cotton Mill South.* Boston: Boston Evening Transcript, 1908.

Hart, T. R. *The School of Textiles.* Raleigh: N. C. State College, N. C. State Print Shop, 1951.

Herring, Harriet L. "Cycles in Cotton Mill Criticism," *The South Atlantic Quarterly,* Vol. 28 (1929), pp. 113-125.

_____ *Passing of the Mill Village.* Chapel Hill: University of North Carolina Press, 1949.

Hoff, G. P. "New Developments and Uses of Nylon," *Rayon Textile Monthly,* Vol. 24 (August, 1943).

Japan Cotton Statistics and Related Data. Osaka, Japan: Cotton Economics Research Institute, 1963.

Josephson, Hannah. *The Golden Threads.* New York: Duell, Sloan and Pearce, 1949.

Kennedy, S. J. *Profits and Losses in Textiles.* New York: Harper and Brothers, 1936.

Kohn, August. *The Cotton Mills of South Carolina.* Charleston: News and Courier, 1903.

Knowlton, Evelyn H. *Pepperell's Progress.* Cambridge, Mass.: Harvard University Press, 1948.

Labarthe, Jules. *Textiles: Origins to Usage.* New York: The Macmillan Co., 1964.

Landrum, J. B. O. *The History of Spartanburg County.* Atlanta: Franklin Printing and Publishing Co., 1900.

Lemert, Ben F. *The Cotton Textile Industry of the Southern Appalachian Piedmont.* Chapel Hill: University of North Carolina Press, 1933.

McPhie, A. "The Changing Structure of the U.K. Cotton Industry," *The Textile Weekly,* May 28, 1965.

Mansberger, H. R., and E. W. K. Schwarz. *Rayon and Staple Fiber Handbook.* New York: Rayon Handbook Co., 1939.

Michl, H. E. *The Textile Industries.* Washington: Textile Foundation, 1938.

Mitchell, Broadus. *The Rise of Cotton Mills in the South.* Baltimore: Johns Hopkins Press, 1921.

Mitchell, George S. *The Industrial Revolution in the South.* Baltimore: Johns Hopkins Press, 1930.

Moncrieff, R. W. *Man-Made Fibers.* 3rd edition. New York: John Wiley Co., 1957.

Moore, A. B. *The History of Alabama.* Chicago: American Historical Society, 1927.

Murchison, C. T. *Cotton Is Sick.* Chapel Hill: University of North Carolina Press, 1930.

"Nylon," *Fortune Magazine*, Vol. 22 (July, 1940), pp. 57-60, 114, 116.

Ormerod, Allan. "The Prospects of the British Cotton Industry," *Textile Recorder*, Parts I-V (Dec., 1962-April, 1963).

———— "Re-equipment in the Lancashire Textile Industry," *The Textile Weekly*, March 23, 1962.

Parker, Margaret T. *A Study of Industrial Development.* New York: The Macmillan Co., 1940.

Schlakman, Vera. "Economic History of a Factory Town," *Smith College Studies in History*, Vol. 20 (1936).

Sherman, J. V. "Textile Research Shows Rapid Growth," *Tax World*, Vol. 97 (Jan., 1947), pp. 135, 204, 205, 210.

Smith, J. F. "Research and the Textile Industry," *Cotton*, Vol. 109 (Jan., 1945), pp. 77-79, 111.

Smith, R. S. *The Mill on the Dam.* Durham, N. C.: Duke University Press, 1960.

Smith, T. R. *The Cotton Textile Industry of Fall River, Mass.* New York: King's Crown Press, 1944.

Snowden, Yates. *History of South Carolina.* Chicago: Lewis Publishing Co., 1920.

The Story of Paper. Washington, D. C.: The Viscose Company, 1944.

Strong, Peter M. "Review of Textile Research," *America's Textile Reporter*, Jan. 26, 1961.

Taussig, F. W. *The Tariff History of the United States.* New York: G. P. Putnam's Sons, 1931.

Thompson, Holland. *From Cotton Field to Cotton Mill.* New York: The Macmillan Co., 1906.

Walton, Perry. *The Story of Textiles.* Boston: Walton Advertising and Printing Co., 1912.

Ward-Jackson, C. H. *A History of Courtaulds.* London: Curwen Press, 1941.

Ware, C. F. *The Early New England Cotton Manufacture.* New York: Houghton Mifflin Co., 1894.

Watkins, J. L. *King Cotton.* New York: J. L. Watkins and Sons, 1908.

Weeden, W. R. *The Economic and Social History of New England.* Boston: Houghton Mifflin Co., 1894.

Whinfield, J. R. "The Development of Terylons." *Textile Research Journal,* Vol. 23 (March, 1953).

Woods, H. F., and F. E. Ackerman. *The Rayon Industry in the U. S.* New York: American Wool Council, 1944.

Young, T. M. *The American Cotton Industry.* New York: Charles Scribner's Sons, 1903.

TABLE XXVII

COTTON-SYSTEM SPINNING SPINDLES IN PLACE, ACTIVE AND IDLE, AND COTTON-SYSTEM SPINDLE HOURS, BY TYPE OF FIBER SPUN; FOR THE UNITED STATES SPECIFIED YEARS, 1920-64; AND BY STATE, 1960-64

Area or State, and Year	Cotton-system spindles (in thousands)					Cotton-system spindle hours (in millions)			
	Total in place at the end of July[1]	Active last working day of year, by type of fiber spun			Idle last working day of year	Total	By type of fiber spun		
		100 percent cotton[2]	100 percent synthetic fibers	Other fibers and blends			100 percent cotton	100 percent synthetic fibers	Other fibers and blends
Alabama:									
1964	1,553	1,419	23	80	31	9,536	8,977	142	417
1963	1,534	1,400	26	73	35	9,290	8,880	133	277
1962	1,540	1,461	30	36	13	9,663	9,292	137	234
1961	1,561	1,427	(5)	[4]66	68	8,597	8,369	118	110
Connecticut:									
1964	103	(5)	(5)	(5)	(5)	346	(5)	(5)	(5)
1963	99	(5)	(5)	......	(5)	294	(5)	(5)	......
1962	98	36	(5)	(5)	53	334	300	24	......
1961	154	46	(5)	(5)	100	379	328	31	20
Georgia:									
1964	2,849	2,477	123	193	56	17,587	15,746	770	1,071
1963	2,865	2,573	106	159	27	17,184	15,723	639	822
1962	2,855	2,642	89	86	38	18,061	16,936	521	604
1961	2,853	2,637	81	82	53	16,397	15,445	483	469
Maine:									
1964	(5)	(5)	(5)		(5)	(5)	(5)	(5)	(5)
1963	241	(5)	......	(5)	28	1,240	(5)	......	(5)
1962	273	232	(4)	[4]4	37	1,347	1,333	......	14
1961	284	246	(4)	[4]5	33	1,668	1,650	4	14
Maryland:									
1964	(5)	......	(5)	......	......	(5)	......	(5)	......
1963	(5)	......	(5)	......	......	(5)	......	(5)	......
1962	(5)	......	(5)	......	......	86	......	84	2
1961	(5)	......	(5)	......	(5)	120	54	52	3
Massachusetts:									
1964	374	67	(4)	[4]74	233	1,140	620	(4)	[4]520
1963	447	153	(4)	[4]130	164	1,482	843	(4)	[4]639
1962	519	205	(4)	[4]114	200	1,019	1,543	15	461
1961	513	414	(4)	[4]71	32	2,259	1,949	13	297
Mississippi:									
1964	(5)	(5)	(5)	......	(5)	(5)	(5)	(5)	......
1963	(5)	(5)	(5)	......	......	(5)	(5)	(5)	......
1962	35	(5)	(5)	......	......	194	176	18	......
1961	37	32	(5)	(5)	......	138	137	1	......
New York:									
1964	(5)	(5)	......	......	......	(5)	(5)	......	......
1963	(5)	(5)	......	......	(5)	(5)	(5)	......	......
1962	25	(5)	......	......	(5)	12	12	......	......
1961	25	(5)	......	......	(5)	20	20	......	......
North Carolina:									
1964	5,814	4,303	607	787	117	37,643	29,256	3,937	4,450
1963	5,751	4,455	599	593	104	35,700	28,632	3,542	3,526
1962	5,661	4,742	468	332	119	36,089	30,863	2,888	2,338
1961	5,658	4,810	429	277	142	32,717	28,599	2,272	1,846

See footnotes at end of table.

TABLE XXVII—(Continued)

COTTON-SYSTEM SPINNING SPINDLES IN PLACE, ACTIVE AND IDLE, AND COTTON-SYSTEM SPINDLE HOURS, BY TYPE OF FIBER SPUN; FOR THE UNITED STATES SPECIFIED YEARS, 1920-64; AND BY STATE, 1960-64

Area or State, and Year	Cotton-system spindles (in thousands)					Cotton-system spindle hours (in millions)			
	Total in place at the end of July[1]	Active last working day of year, by type of fiber spun			Idle last working day of year	Total	By type of fiber spun		
		100 percent cotton[2]	100 percent synthetic fibers	Other fibers and blends			100 percent cotton	100 percent synthetic fibers	Other fibers and blends
Pennsylvania:									
1964	(5)	.....	(5)	(5)	(5)	(5)	.....	(5)	(5)
1963	(5)	.....	(5)	(5)	(5)	(5)	.....	(5)	(5)
1962	(5)	.....	(5)	.....-	(5)	9	.....	8	1
1961	(5)	.....	(5)	.....	(5)	9	.....	9	.....
Rhode Island									
1964	163	(5)	(5)	.....	(5)	428	(5)	(5)	(5)
1963	163	(5)	(5)	.....	(5)	519	(5)	(5)	(5)
1962	230	172	(5)	(5)	(5)	1,207	1,109	8	.....
1961	279	241	.....	.....	.....	1,310	1,306	4	88
South Carolina:									
1964	6,727	5,467	641	527	92	43,852	36,543	4,165	3,144
1963	6,688	5,485	671	439	93	42,955	36,945	3,770	2,240
1962	6,709	5,878	479	247	105	44,505	40,036	3,082	1,387
1961	6,654	6,021	457	138	38	42,298	38,701	2,654	943
Tennessee:									
1964	444	402	(4)	[4] 36	6	2,864	2,658	169	37
1963	441	402	(4)	[4] 31	8	2,736	2,555	148	33
1962	466	408	(4)	[4] 28	30	2,861	2,696	146	19
1961	468	416	(4)	[4] 27	25	2,549	2,418	108	23
Texas:									
1964	213	189	(5)	(5)	(5)	1,142	1,005	(5)	(5)
1963	214	168	(5)	(5)	(5)	1,106	987	(5)	(5)
1962	217	192	(5)	(5)	(5)	1,193	1,147	7	39
1961	215	197	(5)	(5)	(5)	1,172	1,129	7	36
Virginia:									
1964	562	403	(5)	(5)	(5)	3,229	3,161	(5)	(5)
1963	563	514	(5)	(5)	(5)	3,245	3,175	(5)	(5)
1962	566	534	(5)	(5)	(5)	3,418	3,377	20	21
1961	579	540	(5)	(5)	(5)	3,223	3,199	16	8
All Other States:									
1964	520	[3] 654	(3)	(3)	315	2,863	3,842	(3)	(3)
1963	296	538	(3)	(3)	209	1,492	3,197	(3)	(3)
1962	297	272	(3)	(3)	75	1,474	1,344	118	12
1961	323	246	(3)	(3)	88	1,422	1,257	155	10

Source: U. S. Dept. of Commerce, Bulletin 201 (1964), pp. 38-39.

[1] Year ending Aug. 1, 1964, Aug. 3, 1963, Aug. 4, 1962, July 29, 1961, July 29, 1960, Aug. 1, 1949, Aug. 2, 1958, Aug. 3, 1957, July 28, 1956, July 30, 1955, July 31, 1954, Aug. 1, 1953, Aug. 2, 1952, Aug. 4, 1951, July 29, 1950, and July 31, 1920-49.
[2] For 1920-45, includes all spindles consuming cotton at any time during year.
[3] Includes some spindles in "Rest of United States" used in spinning 100 percent synthetic fibers.
[4] "100 percent synthetic fibers" and "Other fibers and blends" combined to prevent disclosure of data for individual companies.
[5] Not shown separately, to avoid disclosure of data for individual companies. Included in United States and area totals.

TABLE XXVIII

WORLD COTTON CONSUMPTION,[1] BY COUNTRY: YEARS ENDING JULY 31, 1939, 1961—64

(Thousands of bales: running bales for United States, equivalent bales of 478 lb. net for other countries)

Country	1964 [2]	1963 r	1962 r	1961 r	1939
North America:					
Canada	435	375	385	335	286
Costa Rica	8	7	5	4	(NA)
Cuba	60	60	60	55	10
El Salvador	33	32	28	25	5
Guatemala	30	30	25	20	4
Haiti	6	6	6	5	(NA)
Jamaica	8	8	8	7	(NA)
Mexico	560	510	510	500	245
Nicaragua	8	7	7	7	(NA)
United States[3]	8,609	8,419	8,954	8,279	6,858
Others	6	6	6	6	....
Total	9,763	9,460	9,994	9,243	7,408
South America:					
Argentina	415	350	485	500	150
Bolivia [4]	10	10	8	10	[5] 7
Brazil	1,250	1,250	1,300	1,250	642
Chile	120	115	110	105	20
Colombia	265	260	245	236	55
Ecuador	20	20	19	18	10
Paraguay	15	15	15	15	(NA)
Peru	90	85	85	80	30
Uruguay	32	23	26	35	1
Venezuela	65	55	50	42	11
Total	2,282	2,183	2,343	2,291	926
Western Europe:					
Austria	117	115	128	127	180
Belgium	385	397	396	427	321
Denmark	47	44	43	44	37
Finland	75	72	76	78	61
France	1,307	1,280	1,312	1,397	1,295
Germany West	1,312	1,306	1,395	1,500	[5] 1,150
Greece	163	155	145	138	85
Ireland	25	26	28	27	....
Italy	1,049	1,064	1,047	1,040	665
Malta	3	....	....	....	(NA)
Netherlands	351	358	356	377	260
Norway	21	20	21	21	15
Portugal	330	320	303	303	100
Spain	550	550	640	580	140
Sweden	98	106	123	131	137
Switzerland	190	190	195	195	141
United Kingdom	1,065	1,025	1,056	1,232	2,690
Yugoslavia	330	330	250	240	92
Total	7,418	7,358	7,514	7,857	7,369
Eastern Europe:					
Albania	30	30	27	27 ⎫	
Bulgaria	250	240	230	215 ⎪	
Czechoslovakia	500	485	490	470 ⎪	
Germany, East	470	460	480	470 ⎬	859
Hungary	300	285	270	255 ⎪	
Poland	600	575	590	575 ⎪	
Rumania	320	310	300	260 ⎭	
Total	2,470	2,385	2,387	2,272	859
U. S. S. R.	6,600	6,300	6,250	6,200	3,809

See footnotes at end of table.

TABLE XXVIII—(Continued)

WORLD COTTON CONSUMPTION,[1] BY COUNTRY: YEARS ENDING JULY 31, 1939, 1961—64

(Thousands of bales: running bales for United States, equivalent bales of 478 lb. net for other countries.)

Country	1964 [2]	1963 r	Year ending July 31— 1962 r	1961 r	1939
Asia and Oceania:					
Afghanistan	45	45	40	40	(NA)
Australia	118	94	94	86	30
Burma	35	30	26	26	(NA)
Ceylon	7	6	6	5	(NA)
China (Mainland) [4][7]	5,500	4,600	4,600	6,800	3,295
China (Taiwan)	275	250	250	210	1
Hong Kong	575	520	510	480	....
India	5,250	4,920	4,940	4,620	3,436
Indonesia	45	55	45	45	2
Iran	185	225	250	200	97
Iraq	35	28	25	23	(NA)
Israel	100	80	70	60	....
Japan	3,164	3,014	3,286	3,441	2,681
Korea, South	330	320	250	270	240
Lebanon	20	20	20	21	(8)
Pakistan	1,240	1,180	1,130	1,125	....
Philippines	165	160	180	135	2
Syria	92	77	73	57	[5] 25
Thailand	95	90	80	70	5
Turkey	560	500	510	500	135
Vietnam, South	65	35	30	25	60
Others	87	80	82	75	39
Total	**17,988**	**16,329**	**16,497**	**18,314**	**10,048**
Africa:					
Congo (Ex-Belgium)	30	40	40	30	7
Ethiopia	35	30	30	25	(NA)
Ex-French West Africa	35	30	25	20	13
Morocco	23	20	12	10	(NA)
Nigeria	45	40	35	30	10
Portuguese Africa	15	13	10	6	(NA)
Rhodesia	25	25	25	18	(NA)
South Africa	140	140	130	110	1
Sudan	30	25	15	5	(NA)
Uganda	25	20	20	17	(NA)
U. A. R.	610	635	596	548	121
Others	10	3	3	3	3
Total	**1,023**	**1,021**	**941**	**822**	**155**
World Total	**47,544**	**45,036**	**45,926**	**46,999**	**30,574**

Source: U. S. Dept. of Commerce, Bulletin 201 (1964), pp. 72–73.

r Revised.
NA—Not available.
[1] Includes estimates for hand-spinning for some countries. Cotton burned or otherwise destroyed is not included.
[2] Preliminary.
[3] 1,000 running bales.
[4] Revised series.
[5] Included others for 1939.
[6] All Germany.
[7] Includes Manchuria.
[8] Included with Syria.

TABLE XXIX

CONSUMPTION OF COTTON, BY END USES, FOR 1962 AND 1963

Use	1962 1000 bales	1963 1000 bales
APPAREL		
Men's, youths', and boys'		
Trousers	850	840
Shirts	735	750
Underwear	350	353
Hosiery	134	135
Overalls and coveralls	105	113
Other	516	466
Total men's, youths', and boys'	2690	2657
Women's, misses', and juniors'		
Dresses	306	278
Blouses, waists, etc.	156	139
Washable service apparel	110	102
Other	533	562
Total women's, misses', and juniors'	1105	1081
HOUSEHOLD		
Sheets	535	566
Towels and toweling	467	476
Drapery and upholstery	277	257
Rugs and carpets	222	200
Bedspreads	186	180
Other	703	695
Total household	2390	2374
INDUSTRIAL		
Industrial thread	180	188
Automobiles	170	170
Bags	124	116
Shoes	119	116
Medical supplies and equipment	90	89
Other	683	737
Total industrial	1432	1416
All uses	8335*	8246†

Source: National Cotton Council of America.

---

* Covers 95% of mill consumption in the United States.
† Covers 98% of mill consumption.

123

TABLE XXX

IMPORTS OF COTTON YARN IN THE SPECIFIED COUNTRIES IN 1938 AND SINCE 1956

(In Millions of Pounds)

Country	1938	1956	1957	1958	1959	1960	1961	1962
Australia	(a) 6.52	5.60	6.88	7.73	6.84	9.08	6.60	N.A.
Austria	3.08	3.20	4.80	4.52	3.88	7.52	8.16	N.A.
Belgium	5.76	8.60	16.24	11.88	15.04	18.44	26.12	N.A.
Burma	(b)16.56	23.88	N.A.	N.A.	N.A.	N.A.	N.A.	N.A.
Canada	4.32	7.32	6.92	6.20	7.52	8.76	7.60	N.A.
Ceylon	0.28	1.52	2.52	2.72	4.52	4.64	N.A.	N.A.
Denmark	N.A.	5.24	5.08	5.92	9.44	8.04	8.80	9.00
Finland (c)	3.68	8.24	6.80	3.76	5.28	6.68	5.04	N.A.
France	0.96	1.20	1.80	0.68	0.52	0.72	0.96	0.92
Germany (West)	45.92	12.88	16.64	19.08	22.96	42.64	33.68	34.20
Greece	1.52	0.16	0.16	0.16	0.16	0.08	0.08	N.A.
Hong Kong	48.04	36.52	39.36	17.76	75.16	56.48	27.32	N.A.
India (d)	30.92	4.00	4.72	2.80	1.44	0.84	0.52	N.A.
Indonesia	16.56	41.92	21.88	32.72	43.00	103.80	N.A.	N.A.
Iraq	N.A.	0.88	0.84	0.84	0.88	1.20	1.04	N.A.
Italy	0.44	0.60	0.52	0.20	0.20	4.64	0.56	N.A.
Malaya	5.56	0.40	0.24	0.24	3.28	4.20	3.04	N.A.
Netherlands	31.64	31.48	32.84	27.40	32.52	36.52	41.04	35.64
New Zealand	0.48	2.08	2.12	2.96	3.00	2.88	3.64	N.A.
Norway	8.20	7.72	9.12	5.16	6.92	7.68	6.96	N.A.
Nyasaland (e)	N.A.	4.60	1.72	3.16	3.20	3.84	4.48	N.A.
Pakistan (f)	....	2.52	1.44	0.68	0.44	N.A.	N.A.	N.A.
Sweden	7.60	7.44	8.72	7.72	11.36	14.84	14.12	14.36
Switzerland	1.68	1.76	6.20	3.68	1.96	1.84	2.56	1.64
United Kingdom (g)	2.20	16.76	14.68	14.56	21.40	38.60	43.68	31.76
Un. of S. Africa (h)	7.44	6.60	5.76	4.48	3.24	5.68	6.04	N.A.
U. S. A.	1.04	0.20	0.16	0.84	1.36	15.12	13.92	28.48

Remarks: (a) Year ending June 30. (b) Year ending March 31. (c) Includes spun rayon yarn and sewing thread. (d) Figures for 1956 onwards exclude Pakistan. (e) Including Rhodesia. (f) Imports on "Private account" only before 1957. (g) Figures from 1959 are not completely comparable with previous years due to changes in classification. (h) Includes territory of South West Africa from 1956. N.A.—Not available.

Source: "Quarterly Statistical Review", The Cotton Board (U. K.)
Arranged by The Cotton Economics Research Institute

TABLE XXXI

IMPORTS OF COTTON PIECE GOODS IN THE SPECIFIED COUNTRIES
IN 1938 AND SINCE 1957

Country	Unit	1938	1957	1958	1959	1960	1961	1962
Austria	Thousands	19.12	41.20	42.04	58.64	76.28	68.80	N.A.
Belgium	Quintals	10.20	65.96	60.60	87.68	95.72	78.32	N.A.
Canada		75.00	244.60	256.24	269.60	281.68	291.28	N.A.
Denmark		71.40	83.04	77.40	92.00	92.32	100.44	103.16
Finland (a)		34.60	29.12	26.24	33.52	37.00	33.76	N.A.
France		5.96	29.36	41.16	20.00	37.52	56.92	56.52
Germany (West)		50.64	153.52	157.00	175.92	287.36	238.92	204.08
Greece		34.20	31.52	34.08	30.76	24.12	29.40	N.A.
Iran		(b)124.64	75.00	79.00	N.A.	N.A.	N.A.	N.A.
Italy		4.88	30.28	19.04	23.56	29.56	29.64	N.A.
Netherlands		(c) 20.32	176.36	155.84	210.28	240.80	263.96	172.92
Norway		54.00	69.44	53.52	64.00	62.00	81.60	N.A.
Sudan		92.96	157.08	136.40	172.36	156.64	196.36	N.A.
Sweden (c)		54.24	92.40	111.76	118.24	133.64	117.04	110.20
Switzerland		28.48	47.16	41.52	42.60	47.20	53.88	55.76
Turkey		120.56	6.24	6.72	0.84	0.24	N.A.	N.A.
Aden	Million	56.32	66.24	46.76	51.60	54.16	53.08	N.A.
Ceylon	Yards	63.48	75.96	90.28	72.84	78.48	N.A.	N.A.
Cyprus		6.96	11.84	6.64	9.44	6.40	8.12	N.A.
India (d)		649.16	11.44	5.08	5.52	4.08	2.28	N.A.
Indonesia (e)		514.88	504.76	287.32	171.04	295.36	N.A.	N.A.
Pakistan		....	3.12	1.16	1.68	N.A.	N.A.	N.A.
Un. of S. Africa (f)		182.16	234.32	190.32	180.75	222.48	179.08	N.A.
Australia	Million	(g)208.64	275.44	299.56	300.44	354.96	261.28	N.A.
Burma	Sq. Yards	(h)137.24	163.24	58.36	114.20	170.20	N.A.	N.A.
Congo		(i) 54.64	68.20	48.40	44.96	39.04	14.48	N.A.
Ghana		N.A.	96.80	66.68	92.08	103.04	108.60	N.A.
Hong Kong		(h) 96.72	280.84	257.08	280.60	321.40	247.76	N.A.
Iraq		60.28	37.40	34.52	43.76	52.92	46.68	N.A.
Kenya/Uganda		61.12	70.88	53.36	63.00	64.92	72.32	N.A.
Malaya		115.00	169.20	150.20	153.24	167.64	176.60	N.A.
New Zealand		29.12	58.36	63.12	61.84	72.08	75.52	N.A.
Nigeria (j)		68.80	149.36	172.48	143.64	210.56	244.84	N.A.
Nyasaland (k)		43.44	46.96	36.00	44.20	49.76	48.44	N.A.
Tanganyika		41.80	48.12	38.24	42.92	40.56	43.36	N.A.
United Kingdom (l)		(m) 51.84	416.28	386.64	537.32	727.72	731.04	575.48
U. S. A.		58.28	126.80	145.84	250.20	464.04	266.24	477.52

Remarks: (a) Includes spun rayon piece goods. (b) Fiscal year ending June 21. (c) Excludes tyre cord fabrics. (d) Figures for 1957 onwards exclude Pakistan. Sea-borne trade only until 1957. (e) Imports on "Private account" only before 1957. (f) Including territory of South West Africa from 1957. (g) Year ending June 30. (h) In Million yards. (i) In thousands quintals. (j) Including British Cameroons. (k) Including Rhodesia. (l) Figures from 1957 are not completely comparable with previous years due to changes in classification. (m) Including knitting. N.A.—Not available.

Source: "Quarterly Statistical Review", The Cotton Board (U. K.)
Arranged by The Cotton Economics Research Institute

TABLE XXXII

U. S. Foreign Trade in Textile Manufactures: Fiber Equivalent, Exports, Imports, and Trade Balance by Fibers, 1920 to 1960

	Exports				Imports				Trade Balance			
	Cotton	Wool	Manmade	Total	Cotton	Wool	Manmade	Total	Cotton	Wool	Manmade	Total
	1,000 lb.	1,000 lb.	1,000 lb.	1,000 lb.	1,000 lb.	1,000 lb.	1,000 lb.	1,000 lb.	1,000 lb.	1,000 lb.	1,000 lb.	1,000 lb.
1920	361,399	17,953	904	380,256	43,916	32,662	210	67,788	317,483	−5,709	694	312,468
1921	210,930	6,275	999	218,204	35,854	44,226	315	80,395	175,076	−37,951	684	137,809
1922	235,413	4,354	1,799	241,566	45,519	42,288	910	88,717	189,894	−37,934	889	152,849
1923	199,058	5,059	1,588	205,705	61,159	48,975	1,020	111,154	137,899	−43,916	568	94,551
1924	200,414	3,933	2,540	206,887	62,811	47,128	633	110,572	137,603	−43,195	1,907	96,315
1925	234,622	3,309	2,317	240,248	48,040	41,056	1,125	90,221	186,582	−37,747	1,192	150,027
1926	231,962	3,326	2,069	237,357	39,163	37,985	1,311	78,459	192,799	−34,659	758	158,898
1927	264,487	3,546	2,278	270,311	40,482	44,972	1,681	87,135	224,005	−41,426	597	183,176
1928	256,921	3,695	2,385	263,001	38,167	43,529	1,402	83,098	218,754	−39,834	983	179,903
1929	260,002	3,770	2,898	266,670	40,505	41,871	1,028	83,404	219,497	−38,101	1,870	183,266
1930	189,627	3,121	2,900	195,648	30,591	26,452	729	57,772	159,036	−23,331	2,171	137,876
1931	162,937	2,030	2,423	167,390	27,069	16,244	641	44,554	135,268	−14,214	1,782	122,836
1932	159,971	1,069	1,597	162,637	24,695	11,814	548	37,057	135,276	−10,745	1,049	125,580
1933	137,480	1,458	1,612	140,550	28,802	14,891	666	44,359	108,678	−13,433	946	96,191
1934	105,227	1,445	1,786	108,458	25,499	11,005	650	37,154	79,728	−9,560	1,136	71,304
1935	91,607	1,532	2,564	95,703	37,069	17,590	831	55,490	54,538	−16,058	1,733	40,213
1936	99,281	1,519	3,975	104,775	60,634	29,583	1,519	91,936	38,447	−28,064	2,456	12,839
1937	124,403	1,884	5,297	131,584	76,550	26,041	2,293	104,884	47,853	−24,157	3,004	26,700
1938	150,552	2,555	5,543	158,650	41,431	13,821	1,281	56,533	109,121	−11,266	4,262	102,117
1939	178,099	2,670	9,054	189,823	58,514	24,807	1,259	84,580	119,585	−22,137	7,795	105,243
1940	179,644	11,170	12,112	202,926	43,155	20,200	779	64,134	136,489	−9,030	11,333	138,792
1941	284,742	7,262	22,244	314,248	29,514	22,408	375	52,297	255,228	−15,146	21,869	261,951
1942	217,680	17,081	15,225	249,986	8,905	20,588	214	29,707	208,775	−3,507	15,011	220,279
1943	271,092	44,428	14,731	330,251	9,380	13,188	124	22,692	261,712	31,240	14,607	307,559
1944	289,025	75,350	20,908	385,283	6,573	14,033	149	20,755	282,452	61,317	20,759	364,528
1945	292,292	56,001	31,000	379,293	25,230	15,527	668	41,425	267,062	40,474	30,332	337,868
1946	376,333	58,900	59,448	494,681	17,604	20,463	1,483	39,550	358,729	38,437	57,965	455,131
1947	758,266	46,088	111,450	915,368	8,422	15,939	514	24,875	749,844	30,149	110,936	890,929
1948	453,824	20,651	93,893	568,368	16,009	42,263	1,232	59,504	437,815	−21,612	92,661	508,864
1949	385,010	10,275	107,349	502,634	18,464	43,399	2,057	63,920	366,546	−33,124	105,292	438,714

Year												
1950	258,666	7,535	81,385	347,586	40,053	63,804	4,348	108,205	218,613	—56,269	77,037	239,381
1951	388,635	8,161	92,063	488,859	33,945	56,387	4,153	94,485	354,690	—48,226	87,910	394,374
1952	337,885	6,067	95,000	438,952	32,416	87,994	3,182	123,592	305,469	—81,927	91,818	315,360
1953	291,223	4,968	96,012	392,203	44,556	61,963	4,638	111,157	246,667	—56,995	91,374	281,046
1954	290,181	5,558	96,349	392,088	48,479	61,052	4,942	114,473	241,702	—55,494	91,407	277,615
1955	262,799	5,514	87,733	356,046	86,958	81,399	6,965	175,322	175,841	—75,885	80,768	180,724
1956	254,559	5,666	92,364	352,589	107,994	91,081	8,801	207,876	146,565	—85,415	83,563	144,713
1957	277,979	4,562	97,651	380,192	95,566	85,173	9,496	190,235	182,413	—80,611	88,155	189,957
1958	250,084	4,577	90,353	345,014	112,138	90,196	13,173	215,507	137,946	—85,619	77,180	129,507
1959	236,430	4,936	96,738	338,104	172,795	126,922	33,628	333,345	63,635	—121,986	63,110	4,759
1960	233,147	4,698	122,926	360,771	255,553	132,132	31,102	418,787	—22,406	—127,434	91,824	—58,016
1961	239,181	4,538	118,944	362,663	188,896	127,458	23,491	339,845	50,285	—122,920	95,455	22,818
1962	220,307	4,369	141,599	366,275	309,848	145,637	30,557	486,042	—89,541	—141,265	111,042	—119,767
1963	207,807	5,589	140,925	354,321	304,312	152,549	36,207	493,068	—96,505	—146,960	104,718	—138,747
1964	213,235	6,998	194,698	414,931	300,276	141,147	49,994	491,417	—87,041	—134,149	144,704	—76,486

Source: Marketing Research Report No. 491, 1920–1960 and Cotton Situation, 1961–1964, U. S. Department of Agriculture.

127